This was all his fault,

yet Drew had slept with her last night, anyway.
Well, he thought angrily, he had never lied to her.
He'd told her he was an architect and a builder. But
he hadn't told Katie the truth.

But if he *had* told her the truth, he might never have
had last night. And he didn't think he could trade last
night with Katie for anything—not even honesty.
Somewhere during the years, he had become so
damn jaded. Then he'd plucked Katie out of the
wind and rain and—

And somehow she and her son had become
everything that was missing in his life.

The Trouble with Andrew

HEATHER GRAHAM POZZESSERE

SILHOUETTE

Sensation

*First published in Great Britain in 1994
by Silhouette Books, Eton House, 18-24 Paradise Road,
Richmond, Surrey TW9 1SR*

© Heather Graham Pozzessere 1993

Silhouette, Silhouette Sensation and Colophon are
Trade Marks of Harlequin Enterprises B.V.

ISBN 0 373 59262 0

18-9408

Made and printed in Great Britain

Other novels by Heather Graham Pozzessere

To Dade County, Florida, and to all those who were touched by the tremendous force of Andrew, and especially to Stuart and Teresa Davant and their son, Charlie, who survived the storm in a closet.

Prologue

Drew should have been in bed, fast asleep for the night. But he had heard his father come in with a few of his friends, and he couldn't resist the temptation to slip into the hallway and listen to them as they sat talking at the dining room table.

His father was at the head of the table, his fingers wound around a cup of steaming coffee. He was a big man, broad-shouldered, with a head full of thick silver hair and hazel eyes that could sparkle with laughter or grow very level and solemn, depending on the occasion. He was as solid as the concrete with which he so often worked—a reliable man, a good man. And Drew knew it well. He adored his father.

Sam Jaffe, slightly younger, his blond hair just beginning to thin, sat next to Andrew Cunningham on his left, morosely drinking coffee, as well. To Andrew's right was Trent Waite, skinny as a toothpick and honest as the day was long. He'd opted for a beer and drank deeply from his bottle, as if doing so would make him forget all the evils in the world. In the last chair at the table, across from Andrew, was Harry Easton, the youngest in their group, in his mid-twenties. He still had all his hair and it was pitch-black.

"They ain't gonna last. They ain't gonna last a damned day if there's the slightest big wind!" Sam said wearily.

Andrew sighed. "I went as far I could go, boys. Hell, I went right to the damned building inspector. I told him they couldn't use those damned staple guns."

"You can't keep causing trouble on the job, Andrew," Harry said unhappily. "We're all going to wind up fired!"

"That's true," Trent said. "We need the work."

"I had to do something," Andrew said. "Harry, folks are going to wind up living in those houses."

Sam exhaled in a snort. "Why, they ain't even building half those places out of real wood. Those walls they were putting up at the project today, they were glorified cardboard."

"They must know what they're doing," Harry protested.

"Bull. We're the labor guys. We know cheap construction when we see it," Sam said firmly.

"I'm telling you," Trent put in. "One big wind and they're gone. All gone. Andrew, there ought to be something we can do about it."

"I told you," Andrew said. "I went to the building inspector. He said everything was right within code, yep."

"Must be a northern fellow," Trent said, tilting back on his chair. "You can build different in the north, a whole lot different. Your problems are different."

Sam snorted again. "It doesn't have anything to do with houses being built in the north or the south. It has to do with those fellows taking bribes from the developers!"

"We can't prove that, Sam," Andrew warned him. He threw up his hands. "I tried. I don't know what more to do. I took it as high as I could. No one is going to do anything differently, and nothing is going to change."

"And we need our jobs," Harry said firmly. "So that's just got to be that. Andrew has to stay out of trouble. What's it to us? We didn't order the materials. I work all day, I need my paycheck when the week is done."

"Saffron Corporation should be sued!" Trent insisted.

Andrew Cunningham shrugged. "One day, they may be. I'll tell you one thing, I'm sure as hell never going to buy one of their houses!" Just as he finished speaking, his eyes narrowed on the hallway. Drew was about to try to slip back into his room, but he realized he had been seen by his father.

"That you, boy?" Andrew asked, a smile curling his lips.

Drew winced, then sighed, coming forward. "Hi, Dad. Sorry. I was just—I'm glad you're home, Dad. Late day, huh?"

Andrew Cunningham still tried hard to hide his smile. "Late day. And boys your age are supposed to be in bed."

"Yeah, right. Well, I guess I'll just go back then. Nice to see you, Mr. Jaffe, Mr. Waite, Mr. Easton. Good night, then."

His shoulders slumped, he headed for his bedroom.

"Son," his father called.

He turned back quickly.

"Come on over here for a minute," his father said, patting his knee. Drew hurried to his father, and Andrew Cunningham, Sr. scooped Andrew Cunningham, Jr. up onto his lap. "You've been listening in, huh?"

Drew nodded quickly.

"It sounds awful, Dad, just awful. The contractor is doing just as cheap a job as he can, not giving a darn about the people who are going to buy the houses."

Andrew arched a brow to his friends. "Smart boy, huh. Well, that's it, Drew. That's it right in a nutshell. They're going to charge big money for those houses, and people may live in them right fine for quite some time. But then one day, who knows..."

"A big wind is going to blow. A great big wind. And those cardboard houses are going to break apart just like matchsticks, you mark my words! It might not be tomorrow, next week or even next year. Hell, it may not even be during the next decade. It may take years, but it's coming," Sam Jaffe warned again. "I was just a kid when the big blow came in '26. Just a kid. But darn, I sure do remember it well! It was worse than anything we've seen lately, and they weren't building cardboard houses back then, mind you!"

"Well, Drew here is never going to build with cardboard," his father said proudly, ruffling his hair. "He already knows what he wants to do. He's going to architectural school, he's going to design the places and see that they're built to his specifications. He's already got the grades."

Sam snorted. "How you gonna pay for one of those highfalutin' schools, Andrew?"

"Andrew's going to quit complaining to inspectors and help us all stay employed, that's how," Harry said flatly. "The kid can't build great houses and get rich, too, you know."

"Maybe he can," Andrew said. "And if not, he can build great houses and just make a good sound living at it, eh? After he gets out of his good school."

Drew was worried. His father worked hard. Long days, into the nights. They did all right. But they weren't rich. Not by a long shot.

"Dad, don't get too fussy on the school, now," Drew told him quickly. "There are lots of good ones

out there, lots of good ones near home, as well, I'm
sure—''

"Harvard. Harvard school of architecture!'' his
father insisted.

"Dad!'' Drew protested. "It's still a long way off.
And I can learn anywhere—''

"And he can, too,'' Andrew said, still speaking
proudly. "Drew, you're going to build fine houses,
you're going to make us all proud. I put a little in, and
then you get rich and famous and look after me in my
old age!''

Drew laughed because his father and the others were
laughing. His father gave him a fierce hug, then set
him on his feet and hurried him off to bed.

He lay down on his mattress and closed his eyes,
listening to the breeze that blew just outside his window. He smiled and started to drift to sleep. He
wanted to grow up to be just like his father. A good
man, a man with principles, a man who didn't keep his
mouth shut when wrongs were being done. His dad
loved houses, and building. He loved to work with
wood, though by trade he was an electrician. Most of
all, he liked to see what men could create together,
from the architect on down.

And Drew loved houses, too. His art teachers had
already told his folks he had talent, and it excited him
to see his visions come to light on paper. That wasn't
the end of it, though, which he knew from listening to
his dad. You had to take a good design and build it
with love and quality materials.

That's what Drew was going to do. He was going to design and build houses. No—homes. Places where people could live happily and safely. Places to do his father proud. And he'd be delighted to look after his dad in his old age...

He drifted, lulled by the breeze rustling through the crotons outside his window. It was a *good* night.

Thankfully, he didn't know that it was going to be his last *good* night for a long time to come.

He had no way of knowing that Sam's wind would come. The big wind. And somehow, blow away a lifetime of dreams.

A wind like none of them had ever seen . . .

Chapter 1

The wind whistled to a higher pitch, groaned, then screamed as if a thousand of Grandma Boyle's banshees were outside creating havoc and terror—and demanding every soul within a radius of a hundred miles. Katie Wells stared blankly at her television, listening while news anchor Bryan Norcross explained to all who could still hear him just what was happening with the storm. She glanced at the clock radio beside her bed. It was 3:13 a.m.

The phone rang and Katie nearly jumped sky-high. Though she still had electricity, she was amazed that the phone was functional while the storm raged outside. She didn't expect the electricity to last much longer.

The ringing came again, grating in her ears. She made a dive for the receiver, thinking that Jordan might still be sleeping. She didn't want to wake him up. Not yet. She might have to wake him soon. There had been so little news about Andrew! Just yesterday morning her father had casually reminded her that there was a small storm off the coast.

And by tonight, the "small" storm that might have found landfall anywhere between the Keys and north central Florida had proven itself to have winds up to a minimum of one hundred and forty-five miles an hour.

And it was heading straight at them.

No, not heading for them anymore, she reminded herself as she cradled the phone receiver in her hand. Hitting them. Hitting them harder with each minute that passed.

"Hello?" she said quickly.

"Katie!"

The booming voice of Ronald K. Wheeler came loud and clear over the wires.

"Hi, Dad," she said softly.

"Katie, you making out okay?"

"I'm fine. I was just sitting here watching the storm report on channel four. Actually, Jordan and I watched television together until about two o'clock— then Jordan said he was sleepy so I thought I'd let him go to bed for awhile. I'm going to give him just a few more minutes—this wind is getting really wild." She hesitated a moment. "You were right, Dad. We're taking a direct hit." She winced. Ron Wheeler had

never minded a moment of "I told you so" in his entire life.

Oddly enough, he didn't sermonize. "I told you to
come up here, Katie."

"And if I'd come up, Dad, Andrew might have
swung to the north and hit Orlando! And Disney
World might claim to be fantasyland, but not even
Mickey Mouse could stop this monster!" She bit her
lower lip, wincing again. How damned stupid to let
him hear that she was beginning to be afraid. Really
afraid.

"Katie, now, you tell me what's going on there—"

"Nothing, Dad, nothing! I've weathered these before, remember? I'm the little kid who followed you
around the house with the C-clamps to board up the
windows all those years ago. You taught me well. I've
got tons of fresh water, plenty of Sterno, enough
canned goods to supply the Red Cross, flashlights,
candles and batteries. We're all set."

"Hmph!" Ron said doubtfully.

The wind whipped again and she braced herself
from cowering. Already, the tenor of the wind had
changed. It was beginning to sound as if a freight train
were coming through her living room.

"Katie, if the wind gets any worse, you pick up
Jordan and you hightail it—"

"Right into the bathroom, I know, Dad. I told you,
I'm prepared. I've got pillows and blankets and everything in there. Candles, flashlights, radio, batteries. In a minute, I'll go grab Jordan and we'll sit out
the rest of the storm in there. Are you happy?"

"No," he said gruffly. "I'd be happy if you were here."

She smiled. What a pain in the hind end! She'd had to go off to college to get him to allow her to stay out until midnight! He still checked on her like a mother hen. But he was a great, very caring father, and she loved him dearly.

She sighed. "Dad, I'm in a Hunnicunn home. They're supposed to be among the very best and safest in the state."

"I know that. I just worry."

"Well, you mustn't—" Katie began, but just as she said so, she heard a sudden monstrous shudder and thundering, as if one of the huge trees on the lot behind her had fallen.

The lights and the television went simultaneously, following a sudden, eerie green glow right on the storm screen.

She swallowed hard, determined to remain calm. She'd already heard a few of the tiles on the roof going. And now the electricity.

She had known the electricity would go; they always lost electricity in a storm. She was prepared. She had candles, flashlights, ice. Batteries, all the right things...

"Katie, Katie! Are you there?"

"Yes, Dad." She forced her voice to be level and light. "Dad, as I was saying, you're not to worry. The power just blew—I think a transformer was blown down nearby. The phone lines will probably go soon,

too, so don't you go getting panicky trying to call me.
I'll call you as soon as I can, okay?''

"I'll be there as fast as I can—"

"No! Dad, you hang tight! Maybe Jordan and I will
take a trip up to see you, if I can take a few days off
work when the winds quit blowing. Listen, Dad, I'm
hanging up now. I want to bring Jordan in here with
me. Believe it or not, I think he's still sleeping. I love
you. Now I've got to go.''

"Katie—"

"Bye, Dad. Talk to you soon!"

She hung up on him, only feeling a little bit guilty.
The electricity was gone, and she was alone in the
darkness—as was Jordan. He was a great kid, but he
was only ten years old. And she was starting to get
darned scared herself.

It was the wind, the sound of the wind. She didn't
think she'd ever heard such a horrible, ripping cry.
And it seemed to go on and on...

"Calm, Katie, calm! It's just that it's been a long
time since you've really heard the wind blow, and you
were a little kid yourself then.'' She spoke aloud, trying to reassure herself. A lot had been different then.
The wind had risen, and she'd crawled up to sit on her
father's lap while it blew. She'd felt instantly safe and
secure.

Well, she was the parent now. And Jordan was
alone.

Just then there was another thunderous crash. A
tree had gone down in back, she told herself. The
sound was deafening.

"Mom! Mom!"

She had barely flicked on her flashlight when she heard her son's high-pitched, panicking voice. She leaped to her feet and ran into the hallway toward his room.

She crashed into him in the hallway. The flashlight catapulted from her hands. Small hands clutched her sleeves feverishly. "Mom, it hit the shutter! That one hit the shutter! I thought it was going to crash right through. I've heard of storms before, but I never heard that they come right inside."

She groped for him in the darkness and shadows, smoothing his sandy hair. "Hey, kiddo, it's all right. We've weathered a whole lot together already, now we'll weather this out, too. The storm isn't coming inside. We bought one of the best houses built. We're going to be just fine."

Even as she said the words, the board she had so painstakingly and carefully clamped over her bedroom window was suddenly wrenched loose, as if a vicious hand had reached out of the darkness of the night to tear it away. Instantly, there came a violent crashing sound. With the board gone, something had come hurtling through her bedroom window.

"Mom!" Jordan said.

"It's just my room."

"It will be soaked and ruined—"

"It's all right. We've got insurance. We're much more important than any room. Let's get into the bathroom, right where we're supposed to be, according to the weathermen, okay? Guess what? I've even got Oreos in there!"

"Wow!" Jordan said admiringly. "That's good thinking, Mom."

She turned him around, starting him toward the hall bathroom. Her home was a beautiful one—Hunnicunn homes were richly detailed in all kinds of architectural features, the finest appliances in spacious kitchens, wonderful, cozy breakfast nooks, master bedrooms with huge baths with skylights and whirlpools, dressing rooms, walk-in closets, the works. But to weather the storm, she'd heard it was best to pick the smallest bathroom in the house with a heavy tub and small windows. That was the hall bathroom, so she had her arsenal there, ready and waiting.

Even as she hurried him along, though, she heard a thunderous pounding on her front door.

"My God!" she breathed. "Someone is out there! In this!"

In the pale glow of her flashlight, she could see her son's beautiful blue eyes widen with alarm. "Mom, you can't go out there."

"I'm not going out there, but someone is in trouble."

"Mom, it could be a mass murderer—"

"In the middle of this storm?"

"Well, you're always telling *me* to be careful."

"And well you should be. But, honey, in the middle of the storm—"

They heard the pounding again. And then a panicked voice, rising even higher than the shrill cry of the hammering storm. "For the love of God! Please, let us in!"

"Get into the bathroom, now!" Katie told her son, all teasing gone from her voice. She had known that storms could be serious, and she had never taken this one as a joke, as a reason for a hurricane party.

She had not imagined it getting this bad, never imagined the feel of wind during this horrible avalanche of fury.

Jordan turned instantly to obey and she tore down the hallway and into the living room, stumbling around the antique furniture she had so painstakingly refinished. She reached the door and heard the cries again, frantic, pleading. The locks were off. She tried to open the door, but the second she did, it slammed in on her with a force that nearly knocked her out, throwing her into the wall like a football hurled across the field.

"Oh, thank you, thank you!" She heard the fervent, feminine cry as a soaked crewful of people swarmed into her house.

The men shouted and pitched themselves against the door to close it once again. Katie was soaked from the rain that rushed in along with the people.

There was one woman, two men and a rain-soaked, panicked child of about six.

"My God, you've saved our lives!" the woman cried. "I thought we were dead, another few seconds and we wouldn't have been able to hold on. My God! The trees! You can't imagine! Even the big ones are falling, crashing all over the place. They're ripping up the sidewalks. Oh, my God . . ."

Even as she spoke, something fell against the house with a horrible crash. The phone began to ring. The little girl started to cry. "There's the hallway," Katie told her sodden, frightened, unexpected guests. "I'll be right there. We'll get towels." She grabbed her living room extension. "Hello?"

"Katie! It's Wanda. I'm in panic, absolute panic!"

Wanda, a friend she worked with frequently, was fairly new to the area. She'd survived a number of blizzards in Montana, but she'd never seen a hurricane before. Katie, close to panic herself, tried to speak reassuringly. "Wanda, get into the bathroom you fixed up—"

"Oh, Katie! Part of my roof has already ripped off! And I'm in the bathroom, but I'm in the wrong one! I got so scared when I heard the ripping sound—now I'm in my bedroom bathroom, and my flashlight and radio and Twinkies and diet soda are in the hallway bathroom!"

"Wanda, you're going to manage without the Twinkies—"

"Katie, the storm is in my house!"

"It's in mine, too. Listen, Wanda, get your mattress into the bathroom with you."

"I have it."

"Then hang in tight! I've got wet strangers in my hallway. I've got to go. Be careful, stay put, keep that mattress over your head, okay?"

"Oh, Katie! I thought the wind would blow—I thought we'd have a rough night, but I never imagined I wouldn't have a home left."

"Hey, we'll get through it. Keep that mattress with you, and watch for the bathroom roof, all right?"

"Right, Katie."

Katie hung up, more worried than she wanted to be. She hurried into the hallway, finding the four wet strangers awaiting her there, wide-eyed as her flashlight hit their faces.

"Come on in here," Katie said quickly, leading them to the bathroom. "I'll get towels." She did so quickly. Jordan had the big flashlight on and the battery-operated radio going in the bathroom. He seemed pretty cool at the moment, lying in the tub, reading a Dracula comic.

"Mom?"

"Some neighbors lost their house," she said.

The talkative woman stuck her head in the bathroom door and saw Jordan. "Hi!" she said, calmer now. "I'm Susan Keogh. I live—I lived two houses down with my daughter, Amy, and my husband." She came in and sat on the toilet seat, and her daughter quickly followed her. Katie handed out towels. "I don't believe this!" Susan said. "I just don't believe this." She was a pretty young woman, Katie realized. It had been hard to tell at first because she was so wet.

"It's more than I remember," Katie admitted. As she handed a big, fluffy towel to the little girl, she was grateful that the bathroom was large.

One of the men came in. Tall, thin, balding, but with a great smile, he offered his hand to Katie. "I'm Ted Barlow. I live on the other side of the Keoghs."

"Nice to meet you," Katie murmured, getting another towel.

"Wow, listen to this!" Jordan told them. He turned up the radio. People were calling in from all over the county.

The dome from the hurricane center in Coral Gables had blown away; places on the highway were devastated. Roofs were flying off right and left, and many desperate people were fleeing for their lives.

"I got in my car in the garage and started moving it out slowly. My sister said, 'Floor it, Donna!', and I did. Then the whole building caved in as we shot out!"

"I live in one of the old guys, made right after that big blow in '26. My home is standing fast, and anyone is welcome to seek shelter here."

"The window blew, the glass shattered everywhere, and once that happened, the roof was gone!"

There was a sudden, horrible grating sound. Susan looked at Katie with alarm.

"It's the roof!" she whispered. "I know the sound."

"My roof can't be going!" Katie said. "This is a Hunnicunn home."

She broke off, hearing the sound again. A few seconds later the other man, Seth Keogh, stepped into the bathroom. "One of your bedroom doors just blew in. If there was a broken window—"

"There was. My bedroom."

"I think your roof is going, too."

"I'll get more mattresses," Katie said.

"I'll help," Seth told her.

"Why don't you stay, and we'll go," Ted suggested.

Katie laughed. Gentlemen! In the middle of the storm. "I know where the mattresses are," she told him.

She started out with one of the small flashlights, the two men behind her. Before she had gone down the hall, she heard the horrible wrenching sound again.

Almost directly above her, the roof suddenly caved in. Water poured down on them.

"Ma'am," Seth said, "I think we've all got to run. This whole place is going to come down!"

He turned back, anxious to reach his wife and daughter. "There's another two houses that seem to be standing all right," he told Katie, "straight across the road."

She aimed her flashlight at the roof in the hallway. Well, what remained of the roof. The rain was blowing in on her. The wind was howling. She couldn't believe it.

There was another violent crash. "Mom!" Jordan cried.

"Jordan!" Katie screamed as she rushed back, not caring that she dropped her flashlight.

The Keoghs and Ted were already on their way, moving down the hall. Jordan came bursting out of the bathroom. "Mom, the roof—"

More of it caved in behind Katie. "Come on!"

She put her arms around her son's shoulders and started running down the hallway, feeling chunks of roof fall behind her.

She passed through the living room.

The room with all her painstakingly refinished antiques. With all those special little baby mementos of Jordan's.

Her cameras were in her bedroom. They were her livelihood. They were insured, and they were replaceable. The pictures were not. Or the ribbons, the newspaper clippings, the baby shoes . . .

"Mom?"

Jordan was the only thing that really mattered. "Let's go, baby!"

Her door was standing open. Seth Keogh was standing there, his whole weight against it, trying to hold it for Katie.

"Ma'am?"

"Coming!"

She was out of her house with Jordan. She followed Seth as he set his hands on his wife's shoulders and started to run with her.

They had said that it wasn't a wet storm. You could have fooled Katie. The water was pouring down on them, the wind so fierce that she could barely walk.

"Crawl!" someone shouted.

She did so, dropping to her knees with Jordan, trying to protect him with an arm.

Things were flying everywhere. Palm fronds, chairs, pieces of cars, tiles from roofs. If they were struck by such an object...

She didn't dare think about it. They had to keep moving.

Something landed with a thud at her side. She stared. It was all that remained of someone's cat.

"Mom—"

"Don't look!" she told Jordan. "Keep moving, follow the Keoghs."

"Mom, I can't see them anymore."

"Oh, God!" Katie gasped. She tried to look into the driving wind and rain. The world was spinning, everything flying, moving. It was so dark, so wet, and she was cold, shivering, terrified.

Then she saw a light.

"There! Jordan, there—that way."

She struggled onward. Inch by sodden inch. Things hit them. Jordan cried out once. "Don't look, don't look, just keep moving!" Katie warned.

"I can't breathe, Mom!" he cried out. "I can't breathe, I can't breathe, I'm not going to make it—"

"Oh, dear God!" she cried. She rose, dragging him with her. She tried to run, tried to see the light, tried to run toward it.

She stumbled and fell. Her foot was trapped in something, she couldn't tell what.

"Mom!"

"Go!" Katie ordered him. "Go to that light! You can get help! Go now."

"I won't leave you!" She could hear the tears in his voice. She could barely see her son's precious face, but she knew that tears joined with the rain sliding down his cheeks.

"Jordan, get help," she began, but then she screamed, for something big and dark was looming over her son.

Her scream abruptly halted. It was a man. A towering man in a huge slicker, coming around Jordan. His hair seemed ink black, slicked back by the rain. He was fairly young—in his thirties, Katie thought—with a strong face and handsome features. Stern features, she decided. She trembled.

She might well be dying, she thought, and she was staring at her rescuer and analyzing him.

He started to reach for her. His eyes were gold, she thought.

Wonderful. She was being rescued by the devil.

She was losing her mind.

"I'll get you up!" he said, his voice deep, harsh, thundering against the wind and rain.

"My foot!" Katie cried.

It was a root, she realized. She had tripped over the stretching root of a fallen banyan, and now she was caught by another root.

He reached down. She noted his hands, long-fingered, broad, very powerful.

He wrenched the root out of the ground.

Katie tried to stand. She started to fall again. He let out an impatient sound and swept her off her feet, pointing across the darkness and grass and uprooted trees and flying debris. "That way, boy! Careful, hurry!"

Jordan turned as he was commanded.

And Katie was carried by her strange, rescuing demon, through the blinding, driving wind and rain and tempest.

Chapter 2

The door to the stranger's house nearly blew from its hinges as he struggled to hold Katie and open it. He shouted a warning to Jordan to watch out as the door slammed hard against the side of the house. Jordan scampered into the house quickly, ahead of the man and Katie.

The man followed Jordan, set Katie down and reached in the blinding wind and pelting rain to get his hands on the door. With an enormous effort, he managed to push it closed.

Her ankle still somewhat sore, Katie stood in his entryway, dripping. Jordan was directly in front of her, dripping as well, and she set her arms around his shoulders, shivering as she waited for their unknown rescuer to turn to her again.

After sliding the bolts on the door, he asked, "Anyone behind you?"

She shook her head.

"I saw others."

"They were ahead. They must have made it to another neighbor's house. They had come to mine when they lost their roof, and then mine began to go, too," Katie told him.

Jordan stepped forward suddenly, causing Katie's arms to fall from around his neck. He offered a hand to the man. "Jordan Wells, sir, and this is my mother, Katherine. Thank you very much for coming to our rescue."

Somewhat humiliated that her ten-year-old son would have thought of such a courteous statement when she still felt herself doing nothing other than staring blankly and shivering, Katie echoed the sentiment swiftly. "Yes, thank you. Thank you so much. You might have saved our lives. I had thought we were safe. We bought a Hunnicunn home..." Her eyes widened as she looked around for the first time.

This house was similar to hers, but different. It was a beautiful house, with cathedral ceilings. A Mexican-tiled, expansive living room was to her left, and across the entry, next to the upper landing on the stairway, was a loft, with a boarded skylight above it. The picture windows in the front of the house were covered with automatic shutters, but the living room was bright, lit by powerful, battery-operated lanterns, one set in the center of a glass-topped coffee table before a deep brown sofa and one on the floor just within the doorway.

She loved her house—had loved her house, she corrected herself—but this one was grander, not more elegant, because there was something very masculine and comfortable about what she had seen so far, but grander. It was a spectacular yet warm and inviting home.

"This must be a Hunnicunn home, too," she said with alarm. "We should get mattresses and hurry into a bathroom."

"This roof isn't going," the man said firmly.

"But—"

"My house will stand."

Katie straightened her shoulders. "That's exactly what I would have said about an hour ago," she informed him with dignity.

He tensed, and she found herself staring at him, frightened by the anger she seemed to have aroused in him. She forgot the house and assessed the man. He was six feet two or three, at least, she thought. Broad-shouldered and probably well-muscled—he was still dripping in a big trench coat. His slicked-back hair was very dark, and his features were arresting, handsome and rugged. His chin was firm and squared, his cheekbones were set wide, and his eyes were not gold but hazel—they merely seemed to burn with a golden fire. He appeared to be in his mid-thirties—perhaps he was closer to forty.

Her words seemed to linger on the air for several moments, then he replied firmly, "My house will stand."

"But how—"

"I was here every day while it was being built," he said. "It will stand." His eyes roamed up and down the length of her, and she realized she was wearing a nightgown. It was white cotton, and although feminine, it was extremely chaste—when it was dry.

Now the garment was sticking to her like a second skin, and the material that had once seemed opaque was all but sheer.

She reached for Jordan again, drawing him against her so she could protect him, or he could protect her, she wasn't sure which. But the hazel-gold eyes of her new acquaintance didn't linger on her body long. They met her eyes again almost immediately.

"I'll find something for you two to put on," he said softly and started toward the stairway, plucking up one of the battery-operated lanterns. Then he paused and turned back. "Perhaps you'd like to come up. The electricity is gone, but there's probably a little hot water left. You—you may want to shower."

Maybe that was why his inspection of her had been so fleeting, Katie thought. She wasn't just covered in water—she was covered in mud. Her hair was plastered against her face, her once-white nightgown was dirty brown, and, of course, she wasn't just dripping on his floor—she was making a filthy mess of it.

Yet, in this storm, who could care about such things? Her host obviously did not. He didn't seem to notice that his floor was being mud slimed. And yet he had noticed her discomfort and shivering. He might have the eyes of a devil and a temper to match, but at least he was courteous.

Katie kept her hands firmly on Jordan's shoulders. "I'd love to—rinse off," she admitted awkwardly, starting up the carved wood stairway with him. "But—" She broke off, wincing as the wind suddenly rose again, shrieking with a greater vengeance than it had before. She heard the pelting of the rain against the house. "I'm not sure such a thing would be wise. The storm is getting worse and worse. We must be right in the height of it."

"Mrs. Wells, I assure you again, this house isn't going anywhere. And I wasn't suggesting that you jump into the Jacuzzi and run the jets for an hour, but the storm may last some time, and you both must be very uncomfortable. I think you'd be safe hopping quickly in and out of the shower. But you certainly must suit yourself. I'll show you to the guest room and bath, and you may shower or take your mattress into the bathroom. Truly, it is your choice."

He listened, Katie thought. He had remembered her name from Jordan's quick introduction. And his confidence was contagious. She could still hear the awful howl of the wind, but oddly, she felt protected here. She felt safe. Why should she? Her house had crumbled. He said he had been here every day when his house had been constructed, and that implied he knew something about building. She could hear the drone of a battery-operated radio or television from somewhere, so he had to be aware of the extent of the storm.

"Come on, Mom." Jordan started to step away from her. Not at all sure of what her bedraggled gown and mud still covered of her body, Katie hurried behind him up the stairway, following their host as he led them to the first door off the loft landing.

The lantern illuminated an exquisite room. The floor was hardwood, with a beautiful Persian carpet set at the foot of the bed. There were all kinds of intricately carved built-in cupboards, an entertainment center, bookcases and curio stands.

There were French doors at the rear of the room—boarded over now—but she was sure they would look over a pool and patio area. And there was another door, leading to the right, off the room.

Their host led them to an elegant guest bathroom, much like the master bathroom in her own home. There was a huge, black sunken tub with whirlpool jets and gold fixtures. The floor was red, black and white tile, and the commode and sink were also black. There was a shower in the corner to the left of the tub, and bloodred towels and washcloths hung from a rod nearby.

He set the lantern on the floor between the bedroom and bath and strode to one of the dark wood doors of a walk-in closet. He pulled out two terry robes, both adult sized, and tossed them on the bed, which was covered with a plush comforter that continued the colors of the bath—red, black, gold and white—in plaid.

"Sorry, I haven't anything smaller," he apologized to Jordan, and Katie decided she liked him for the first time as she watched him talk to her son. He seemed different. Not angry, not hard. His mouth curved into a smile, and she realized that he was really an attractive—very attractive—male. An uneasy chill seized her, but he ruffled Jordan's tawny hair and turned to leave the room. "I'll be downstairs. I have a small battery-operated television down there, if you'd like to see what's going on. And," he continued, almost as if offering an added inducement, "I have Sterno and hot coffee."

He left, closing the door behind him.

"Wow!" Jordan gasped. "What a house!"

"Yes, but it doesn't matter what it looks like," Katie said quickly. "Our house was great. *Was,* Jordan. I think we ought to be in a bathtub with a mattress over our heads—"

"Mom, you have mud all over your face."

Mud on her face shouldn't have meant a damned thing at this moment. And it didn't, really. Yet she found herself heading into the bathroom and looking into the huge mirror above the sink. The lantern light wasn't bright, but it was enough to show her that she was covered with mud.

Without thought she turned on the faucets and began to splash water at her face.

"Mom," Jordan said.

"What?" She paused.

"Listen."

She did listen. The wind still howled. Viciously. It was somewhere between four and five in the morning, she thought. The storm was at its worst.

"It's awful—"

"It's awful, yes, but you know what you don't hear?" Jordan asked her.

"What?"

"No boards ripping off—he has good shutters on this place. No ripping sounds—his roof is staying on. Mom, please, will you let me hop under the shower for just a minute?"

She hesitated. "For just a second."

Jordan happily shed his wet, muddy clothes, and Katie realized that her son had been shivering. It was summer, and the days had been wickedly hot, and their host must have been running an air conditioner full blast until the electricity had gone. The house was cool, almost cold. This strange, wild night was cool, as well, so wet, so wind-tossed.

That would all change soon enough, Katie thought. The promise of summer days with no air-conditioning in Miami was frightful.

If they survived. If they just survived the night.

But Jordan was right. Nothing was ripping from the windows. And nothing was ripping from the roof.

"All right, hop in, quick," she told Jordan.

Jordan wasted no time. At ten, he was becoming a modest individual, and she tried her best to respect his privacy, but at the moment, he didn't seem to care. He whipped off his clothes, his back to her, then jumped into the shower stall.

"Wow! There's hot water left!" he cried.

"Save me some then," she heard herself say.

A few seconds later, Jordan was out, wet and squeaky clean, reaching for one of the bright red towels. Katie handed one to him, noting that they were embossed with the initials AGC.

He still hadn't introduced himself. Actually, he hadn't even said that it was his house.

It had to be. Why else would he have been so concerned with details while it was being built?

"Mom, there's still hot water," Jordan said. Wrapped in the red towel, he headed for the bedroom and one of the oversize robes.

"Don't go far!" Katie called out, alarmed. Jordan was all she had in this world. Maybe this house was safe, but she still didn't want to take any chances with Jordan.

She stepped quickly into the shower stall and stripped off her sodden and muddy garments. She planned on turning the water on and off, but there was a bottle of shampoo and conditioner in one of the little gold soap stand, and she could have decent hair in a matter of seconds. And the water was still delightfully hot.

For a moment, she almost forgot that the wind was tearing apart her city. It was such luxury just to feel the warm water.

But then she came to her senses, rinsed quickly and stepped from the shower. She did feel better. A hundred times better. She wrapped up in one of the red towels, then found Jordan waiting for her just outside the door. He was wearing a white robe. Too big for him, yet oddly not that huge. It might have been a woman's robe, perhaps. She was sure he wasn't very happy about it.

He grimaced at her. "I tried the black one. But I step all over it. I imagine I'll be lots taller than you one day, but for the moment, well, mind this one?"

She grinned, taking the black terry robe he handed her and wrapping it around her before letting her towel fall to the floor. "Give me your towel, Jordan," she said, swooping down to pick up her own. "I don't want to leave this place a mess."

Jordan handed her his towel. He was grinning. She paused. "What?"

"You're afraid to take a shower in the storm, but you don't think twice about cleaning up!" Jordan teased.

"It isn't our house."

"Yeah, but I'll bet he has a maid to come in and clean for him," Jordan said.

"It doesn't matter, it isn't our house—"

"And we really should impress him, huh?"

"No," Katie protested indignantly. "We just shouldn't be piggy, that's all. Especially in the home of someone who pulled us out of the storm."

Jordan shivered suddenly, staring at her. "Wow, Mom. That was awful! The wind, the rain! I couldn't breathe, I really couldn't breathe. I've never been so scared."

"I know. I was scared, too."

"Really scared?"

"Right out of my wits."

"We could have died!" Jordan said.

They could have, Katie reflected. She could hear the wind. The brutal, slashing, destructive, furious wind.

Jordan shivered again. "Oh, Mom—"

"It's all right. That part of it is over, and really, we're out of it now."

But they weren't. Not really. Maybe this house would stand. No matter how hard she tried not to, she could still hear the cries and moans and shrill screams of the wind. The rain was coming harder, too.

"Let's get downstairs quickly," she said. She finished picking up, folding their wet and muddy clothes and trying to leave them as neatly as possible in a corner of the bathroom.

Then she ran her hands absently over the robe and realized there were initials on the pocket.

Once again, she found the embossed letters AGC. Well, whoever he was, AGC made a nice income.

She heard the wind beating against the house as they started down the stairs. Chills swept through her, and she decided that since she couldn't ignore it, she was going to have to learn to listen to it. She tightened her jaw, determined she wasn't going to let her son feel her shaking. But even as the feelings of security stole over her, she couldn't forget the terror of running through the storm. She would never forget the awesome power of it.

She found their host in the large living room, seated on the chesterfield, staring at the small screen television. He had changed, too. He was dressed in faded jeans, a knit polo shirt and Docksiders.

He looked from the television to the two of them, his eyes roving up and down them but betraying no emotion. Then the corner of his lip curled just a bit.

"You decided to shower, I see."

"Yes. Quickly," she told him.

He nodded, then stood, sweeping a hand toward the sofa. "Take a seat. You can see something of what's going on."

Katie sat, and Jordan joined her. The news anchor was sending out warnings about what to do when your roof went or your windows caved in. There were reports from people who called in. Terrible reports, some about horses and cattle, that had flown right through the windows to land in their owners' living rooms.

She was staring at the television in horror when she heard her host speak again. "It's been so long since we've really been hit this hard, no one prepared for this storm. People didn't board up. They didn't prepare."

"I prepared," Katie muttered bitterly. Those golden eyes looked at her hard, and she wondered at the brooding anger in them.

Then she realized that he was holding mugs, and he passed one to her. "Coffee. Hot. Black. If you want something in it—"

"No, no, that's fine, thank you very much," Katie said quickly. She accepted a cup from him, then he offered the other to Jordan. "Hot chocolate. Hot. Brown. No marshmallows, sorry."

Jordan grinned and took the mug from him. "Great. I'll manage without the marshmallows."

Their host turned and walked out of the living room. Jordan followed his departure with his eyes.

"Nice guy, Mom. Flirt a little."

"Jordan, we're in the middle of a major disaster. And we don't even know this guy's name. I mean—"

"Right, right. He's a stranger, we don't know if he's sane, we don't know anything about him. But he has a great house—and he keeps hot chocolate. What more do you want?"

Jordan was teasing her, and she was glad. Looking into his eyes, she saw the sparkle in them, and she was grateful that children could be so resilient. Of course, they had been lucky.

They had been rescued.

And by this man.

He came into the room again and she quickly stared at the television, yet she was certain he knew that they had been speculating about him. He brought his cup of coffee with him this time and sat down beside Katie, sipping the hot brew. He looked at the television again, and they all listened as the weather reporters tried to ascertain just where the storm was doing the greatest damage.

He turned, meeting her eyes, and Katie realized that she had been staring at him again. She blushed, but then said bluntly, "My son came in and introduced the two of us. If you don't mind, what's your name?"

He winced. Looked at the television, stared at her, hazel eyes glittering. "Andrew," he said. "Andrew Grant Cunningham."

"Oh!" Katie said.

Jordan started to laugh. "Andrew!" Then he sobered quickly. "It's a great name. I mean, usually it's a great name. I have a few friends named Andrew."

"Right," Andrew Cunningham said, and as usual, when he was talking to Jordan, he seemed to smile. "I guess all of us will have a hard time of it for a while. But I go by Drew. You can call me that."

"Then there's always Mr. Cunningham," Katie advised.

"Yeah, sure," Jordan agreed.

"You don't need to call me Mr. Cunningham. Drew will do just fine," their host told him firmly.

"Drew," Jordan agreed. Katie had been outvoted.

Jordan took a long swallow from his mug, then looked at the coffee table, then at his mother. "I'll take it," she told her son. "If you'll point me toward the kitchen—"

"Just give it to me."

"I don't want to put you out—"

"You're not putting me out!" he said with exasperation, taking the mug and striding away.

"You seem to make him mad easy, Mom," Jordan told her.

That seemed true enough. She didn't reply, though, because Drew Cunningham was returning, taking his seat beside her again, staring at the small television.

Katie suddenly felt Jordan ease down beside her.
"Can I put my head on your lap, Mom?"

"Sure," she said, and he did so. She ran her fingers
through his tawny hair and became more acutely
aware of the man beside her than she was of the wind
and rain. He was very well built, broad-shouldered,
muscled. His hands were large, fingers very long, nails
clean and neatly clipped, and yet she noticed that his
palms were callused, as if he was accustomed to man-
ual labor. He was tanned, his face nearly bronze and
very handsome with near-gold eyes and very dark hair.
He was, she decided at last, young—young enough,
anyway—very good-looking, certainly in good shape,
and certainly financially sound. And he had an almost alarmingly sensual scent. A clean, masculine
scent with a very subtle hint of after-shave or co-
logne.

Someone should have latched on to him by now, she
found herself thinking, and then she realized she was
staring again and looked quickly at the television.

"Everyone was out of your house, right?" he asked
her suddenly.

She nodded.

"You and the boy live alone?"

"Yes," she told him. And then she decided she
might as well ask a few questions herself.

"You live here alone?"

"Yes."

"It's so strange. I never knew any of my neighbors
before. And now, tonight..."

"There are only seven houses in this cul-de-sac," he reminded her. "And since the invention of garage-door openers, people come and go through their garages and sometimes never see one another. I think your son has fallen asleep," he finished suddenly.

Katie looked down. Jordan's eyes were closed. His lips were slightly parted. He was breathing easily.

She wished she could do the same.

"Listen," Drew Cunningham advised her.

"What?"

"The wind. It seems to be dying down some."

She did listen. She couldn't tell at first, but then she looked at the television and listened as the weather reporter said the storm was beginning to move on. It could weaken as it crossed the state, but those in its path must beware.

There were warnings about going outdoors, warnings about electric wires, pleas that people stay home and off the roads so crews could work and emergency vehicles could get through.

"Want more coffee?" Drew asked her.

"I'll get it."

"Your little boy is sleeping," he reminded her.

She handed him her cup. He came back with more coffee for them both.

She would have liked to see the kitchen. She wondered if the room would give her any idea if there had been a Mrs. Cunningham somewhere along the line.

It was none of her business, of course.

And once again, she found herself thinking that he was just too attractive, even if he could be gruff and almost rude. There had to be a woman.

He was a stranger who had saved her, and that was all.

"Listen again," he told her. "It's almost died down."

It was still there—but he was right. The wind whistled softly. It wasn't shrieking anymore.

"I'm going out," he told her, setting down his coffee cup, rising.

"Wait!"

He hesitated and she eased Jordan's head to the sofa, then rose swiftly with him.

"Why don't you let me—"

"I want to see," she told him firmly.

He shrugged and made his way to the front door. He opened it and stood a moment, then started out.

She glanced at her wristwatch—waterproof, thankfully—and saw that it was just after seven o'clock. With the robe tightly bundled about her, she followed Andrew Cunningham outside and into the slow-dawning light of day.

The rain continued to drizzle; the wind would be silent, then sweep around her in a gust, then go still once again.

Massive trees lay everywhere, the roots having ripped up earth and grass and asphalt and concrete. Branches lay strewn everywhere.

Power lines were down. They cracked and sizzled, and Andrew Cunningham barked a quick warning to her. "Don't even go near one of those wires."

She bristled. She wasn't stupid. She knew that contact with one of the wires could fry her.

She had barely stepped off the porch, and she was seeing all she thought she could bear to see. Her house stood across the way, across a jungle of trees and bushes and newly created, wildly twisted trash. Bits and pieces of automobiles were entwined with the downed foliage. Someone's awnings lay scattered across a pile of branches.

Clothing, some of it brightly colored, added a strange touch to the rubble. Everything was everywhere. Desks lay strewn about; drawers had flown out and cracked open. Kitchen utensils lay upon the earth, and someone's television lay amid a pile of muddied socks.

Roof tiles and shingles were everywhere. There didn't seem to be an unlittered piece of earth anywhere near them. Some palms were half down, looking like strange, naked skeletons in a death dance. It was horrible.

The storm was, for all intents and purposes, over. At least here. It would be moving across the state, still strong enough to wreak havoc in the Everglades and pay a brutal visit to the west coast. But here its damage had been done.

Yes, it was over.

But the disaster it had created was just beginning.

Chapter 3

There were seven houses, each on an acre, in the once pretty cul-de-sac, on a drive that had come around a small circular park of trees and foliage.

The massive banyan was down, and the earth and the road were ripped up along with it. It was along the path Katie and Jordan had taken from their own home to Andrew Cunningham's.

The banyan had nearly done her in during the storm. While she'd still been home, she would have gladly ripped it straight out of the ground herself. Now, she was sorry to see its destruction. Somehow, it was sadder to see the majestic tree even more destroyed than her own home. It had been such a beautiful old tree. The builders of the place had obviously taken great pains to go around it. Now their pains didn't seem to matter much.

Nor did much else. Of the seven houses, four remained standing and seemed almost absurdly untouched. The three others, including her own, were wretchedly damaged. The boards she had put over her windows were gone—as were her windows. Her roof had all but disappeared in several places. The structure was still standing.

She needed to take pictures. All of this needed to be put on film.

But her cameras were inside that shell of a house, along with most of her film and a number of her best pieces. Maybe something was left. She needed to get in to see.

"Wow!" she heard suddenly. She turned quickly. Len Hampton, a retiree from New York City, had come out of his house, which was still standing and was next to Drew Cunningham's. His wife, Sophie, a sweet, petite little lady with a lot of fire and gumption, came up behind him, her silver hair in a perfect coiffure, as if she hadn't tossed a single moment throughout the long night. They were a nice couple, very pleasantly old-fashioned, and Katie had met them because Sophie had dragged Len over with a thermos of coffee and a pound cake the day Katie had moved in. The couple hadn't said a word about any of their neighbors. They had been friendly, telling her about themselves, and said she must feel free to visit or ask for any kind of help any time.

"Wow!" Len repeated, turning to Katie and Drew. He looked across the cul-de-sac at what had been Katie's house, then he stared at her hard, his amazement turning to worry. "Katie, you okay? What are you doing over here? What about your little boy?"

"Len, obviously Katie's here because..." Sophie said, extending a hand to indicate that there wasn't much left of Katie's house.

"Oh!" Len said.

"It's all right, Len. Jordan is inside, sleeping," Drew said, and Katie nodded, smiling.

"Yes, we're fine, thank you."

Even as they spoke, they saw Brandon Holloway and his wife, Midge, come running from across the street. They were the only other neighbors Katie had met before the storm. The newlyweds had the smallest of the cul-de-sac houses. Midge was cute, a petite young woman with shoulder-length curly dark hair, a gamine face and velvet brown eyes. Brandon was about five ten, with a serious young face, sandy hair and a nice build.

Katie didn't feel quite so out of place once the Holloways had arrived—odd to feel improperly dressed under the circumstances—since the Holloways were both in terry robes, as well. They both wore sandals, while Katie's feet were bare.

"My God!" Brandon cried. "You all right, Katie? I've never seen anything like it. Your roof is half gone, you know. Your windows are shattered, your house—"

"I know," Katie said.

"Brandon, you don't have to get quite so descriptive," Midge advised softly.

"Oh!" Brandon said apologetically. "It's just in such bad shape, I hope that you and Jordan—"

"It's all right," Katie said, "we're fine. Jordan is sleeping inside Mr. Cunningham's house."

"They're both fine," Drew said.

"Thank God! We were so lucky!" Midge said, her dark eyes wide. "We seem to have lost a few roof tiles, and the darnedest thing—our shed has disappeared. Just disappeared."

"No, Mrs. Holloway, it didn't disappear," Len said quickly.

"I don't think so, anyway," Sophie said.

"Then where—" Brandon asked.

"There's a shed sitting in our side yard," Len told him.

"I did keep telling you that I wanted a shed, Len," Sophie said, her eyes twinkling.

"Well, it seems like you've got one," Brandon said. "Mine!"

"Young man, you're welcome to take it back," Sophie told him. "Any time. It's not in great condition."

"Nothing is!" Midge noted.

"Things don't matter terribly. They can always be replaced somehow," Drew said. "But we're missing a few people. Excuse me. The Keoghs and Ted Barlow were rushing into the Thomason home when I found Mrs. Wells and Jordan out here. I'm going to go over and see that they're all okay."

Katie started to follow him, then gritted her teeth, nearly gasping as she stepped on a piece of broken, twisted metal. It looked like a part from a car, she thought fleetingly.

Midge had been watching her. "Katie, wait, I'll get you some shoes."

"That's all right, Midge. You're so tiny—"

"And she has flippers for feet," Brandon supplied cheerfully. Midge stared at him. "Sorry!" he said quickly.

Midge grimaced. "All right, so I'm small, my feet are not. My shoes are an eight and a half, Katie."

"Perfect," Katie told her. Katie wore an eight, but she wasn't about to say that her feet were a half-size smaller than Midge's, not after Brandon had called his wife's feet flippers.

Midge ran to her house while Katie waited with Brandon, Len and Sophie in the debris-strewn yard. They could still feel the wind, and the sky remained an ominous shade of metallic gray. It would start to rain or drizzle again in minutes, Katie knew. But like Drew Cunningham, they were all worried about the fate of the rest of their neighbors.

Drew returned, running from the southern edge of the cul-de-sac, before Midge could acquire the slippers, and though his features remained taut, his look somewhat grim, he still seemed relieved. "The Thomasons came through just fine—Lucy doesn't think they lost any roof tiles, but I think she has to be wrong there. Ted, Susan, Seth and Amy are all fine, too—Susan says they're not coming out just yet.

They're going to stay with the Thomasons for awhile, since they have a daughter just a year older than Amy. Until—until we find out what the hell happened here and their home is rebuilt.''

"That sounds fine,'' Sophie said enthusiastically. "Ted Barlow can come over and stay with us—he and Len both love a good game of cribbage after dinner.'' Sophie looked enthused, as if the idea was appealing. "Oh!'' she said, turning to Katie. "Of course, dear, you and Jordan are welcome, too. I'm just not sure—''

"Katie can stay in my den or the weight room,'' Brandon suggested.

"Mrs. Wells and her son are welcome to remain in my house, for just as long as necessary,'' Drew said firmly.

"But—'' Katie began.

"Here we are!'' Midge called cheerfully, running back. "Shoes, Katie, a choice of them!''

Midge had brought over several pairs, black loafers, white sneakers and beige pumps. Katie had to grin, thinking of herself dressed for business in Drew Cunningham's terry bathrobe and Midge Holloway's pumps.

"Midge,'' Katie told her, "thank you, but really, I don't need so many, and I am insured.''

"Katie,'' Brandon said, "she'll never know they're gone. She has more shoes than a shoe store.''

"And really, dear,'' Sophie said practically, "just what are you going to do? Run around barefoot until you're able to make the insurance claim?''

"Good point," Len noted proudly.

"I concede," Katie said. "Though there just may be something left in my house. Midge, thanks," Katie told the woman. "I'll return them just as soon as—" She broke off, wondering when "just as soon as" was going to be.

But it didn't matter what she might have said. Just then, the wind seemed to take off with a sudden, whimsical whistle, and the rain began to fall once again. Sophie shrieked and waved a hand, grabbing Len by the shoulder. "See you later!" she called.

"Ditto!" Brandon said, setting his hands on his wife's shoulders and turning to make the run across the street.

"Come on," Drew Cunningham told Katie gruffly. The rain was beginning to pelt quickly. He set a hand on Katie's back to guide her across the destroyed lawn. She was startled by the jolt of sheer electricity that seemed to streak through her with that simple touch. Maybe she shouldn't have been surprised. She had found him arresting from that first moment when she had lain among the banyan roots and he had reached a hand down to her and stared at her with eyes that seemed pure gold and fire.

She hurried ahead of him and into the house. He followed behind her, closing the door. "I imagine it will be like this off and on for awhile now," Drew said.

"I imagine," Katie said. "Still..."

"Still what?"

She'd been about to say that she really needed to get into what was left of her house no matter what the sky was doing. But she decided to wait awhile. She had the distinct impression that he would try to stop her, that he would tell her the structure was unsafe, that he would do something to hinder her efforts. He was one of *those* men, she thought. Accustomed to giving orders—quietly, politely, of course, but in one of those voices no one thought to disobey. He seemed to be the confident sort, assured in his knowledge and judgment.

Not that she meant to be stupid. She was now more than ever aware that her life was worth far more than anything in the house. She didn't intend to leave Jordan an orphan. But she was fairly confident—and competent—herself, and she knew how to be careful.

Still...

"I wonder if the real brunt of the storm is over," she said.

"Let's see what they're saying now," Drew suggested.

They went to the sofa, not soaked but a little dusted with raindrops. Jordan was still sound asleep, sprawled out and taking up most of the space on the chesterfield, which left Katie very little room when she sat next to Drew. Their thighs touched. She stared at the television, listening to the voice of Mayor Suarez. He was pleased that downtown Miami seemed to have escaped the storm. The skyscrapers had held; from what the mayor could see, there were some blown-out windows, but not much more.

Yet right after the mayor spoke, they heard from reporters moving southward down Route 1. The tales they were telling were devastating and grew worse as the reporters made their slow trek down the highway. Not a single traffic light was working. The road was blocked by trees, by downed poles, by such ridiculous things as household appliances. The farther south they went, the worse it was. They were beginning to estimate that certain areas had been hit with winds raging over two hundred miles an hour.

Another report came in, assuring people that emergency services would be available. Shelters were listed. Katie realized that thousands of people in the area were homeless.

"What a horrible, horrible storm," she whispered. "No wonder my house went down."

"The house shouldn't have gone," he said curtly.

Katie stared at her host, wondering at the fury and tension in his voice and startled by the angry look he gave her.

Especially since Jordan's manner of sleeping had forced them to sit so close together. She was alarmingly aware of him once again, aware of the heat and fire that seemed to radiate from his form and sweep her with warmth. She was aware of the hard-muscled structure of him, of the thighs pressed against hers. Very aware of his locked jaw and the burning gold of his eyes. His house was still standing. Why was he so angry?

She was the one with nothing left.

"Why are you snapping at me?" she asked him. "It's hardly my fault my house went down."

"I'm not snapping!" he said.

But he was. Definitely snapping. And she should have been angry in return—she was angry. But she was also alarmed, and worried about herself. Despite his anger, she found herself still fascinated by the heat of his proximity, by the feel of his thigh hard against her own. She could almost imagine that his jeans and the terry robe were both gone, that she could feel his flesh . . .

She jumped up, her cheeks burning, her heart pounding, shocked at her suddenly active hormones. He was an attractive man, she had long ago admitted that. All right, so her life hadn't included many attractive men, or perhaps it had, at times, but none of them had ever made her feel this way, and perhaps she hadn't wanted to feel this way. She'd been busy. Raising Jordan, making a living. And really, the only time she ever thought about having a man in her life was when her father was around to torture her, with the eternal "you're still young, Katie" comments, the "I have a friend I want you to meet at dinner." Ron Wheeler was also fond of reminding her that she wasn't dead and that she didn't have any right to act as if she was, which wounded her, because she considered herself very busy. Jordan was into everything. He loved baseball, soccer, football and video games. He had school projects and homework. And she had her own work, which she loved. Long ago, Terry had encouraged her, and she had learned that she loved photography so much because she really had a good eye and could capture bits and pieces of life on film.

For a long time, it had seemed that Jordan and photography were all that she really had to hang on to.

And so she had hung on to them. Which had been easy. Because nothing had tempted her to stray from the course. But now...

She was tempted.

Her father, she was certain, would dance in the streets.

Yet she wondered how she could be feeling such things, thinking such things, when her world had just been blown to bits. There was devastation out there, she reminded herself.

This man could even be married!

Old argument, a voice inside her said, then demanded, *if so, where is his wife?*

Out of town?

Smart people, she was suddenly certain, were out of town. And if he had a wife, she was probably smart.

No, nothing had indicated that he might have a wife.

Standing, she stared at his left hand—not that that would be any guarantee. But he wasn't wearing a wedding ring.

And he was staring at her as if she had lost her senses.

"What is the matter with you?" he asked her.

"Nothing. You *were* snapping."

He threw up his hands. "Well, if I was snapping, I'm sorry, but you shouldn't worry—I don't bite. You're not in danger."

Katie wasn't so sure. But she was standing in his grand living room, in his robe, with Midge's shoes clutched to her chest as if she was about to take flight. Jordan remained on his sofa, sleeping as if he hadn't a care in the world.

"You can put those shoes down, you know," Drew advised her.

She dropped the shoes, then realized she had dumped them all over his floor. It had been an immaculate floor, she was certain.

Until she and Jordan had dripped all over it, of course.

"Sorry," she murmured, shaking her head. "I need to put these somewhere out of the way. For the time. I mean, of course, we really can't stay here—"

He leaned closer to where she knelt to retrieve the shoes. "Mrs. Wells, there aren't that many choices. You've heard the news. The shelters were overcrowded last night. And if all these reports are half true, tens of thousands of people are homeless. You have to stay somewhere."

"Jordan and I don't want to impose—"

"It's no imposition!" he roared, exasperated.

Macho man, Katie thought again.

"I'm not quite sure it's the right thing to do," Katie murmured. "Your family—"

"I'm not married, and I don't have children, and anyone I know and care about is an intelligent individual who can see that your home is not habitable and may never be. If you're uncomfortable about the arrangement, I have an office I can move into."

"No!" Katie protested, horrified. "I would never think of putting you out of your home—"

"You might," he murmured wearily, leaning back.

"What?"

He inhaled and exhaled. "Mrs. Wells, you're very welcome to stay here. I'll leave if you like, I'll stay if you like. You can take the guest room, and Jordan can have the room to the left of it—there's an entertainment center in there with a stereo system, television, even games. Assuming we get electricity again some time in the near future. Both rooms have private baths. I'm sure you'll be as comfortable as possible out of your own domicile. I can almost guarantee you that I won't be around very much, not with the cleanup that's going to have to go on now."

"But—"

"Will you please quite worrying?"

Katie hesitated. The offer was a darned good one. Her choices were limited. She could go to a shelter and sit there endlessly, chewing her lip, biting her nails, wanting to be doing something.

In a few days, of course, she could go to her father's. She loved her father.

And she could listen endlessly to him telling her that she was young, that she needed to get herself a life that didn't include other people's joys and devastations in black and white and color film.

She could stay in the Holloways' weight room.

Or join Ted at Sophie and Len's. Poor Ted. He'd wind up on a couch, of course, to give her and Jordan a room.

Here, she was right across from her own home. She could be here when the insurance adjusters and the repair people came. She could watch what happened.

She could dig through the rubble.

The rubble...

She needed to start digging right now.

"Mr. Cunningham—"

"If you are going to stay, please call me Drew. Mr. Cunningham gets irritating after a while."

"Well, then, excuse me!" she said, with just a note of sarcasm to her voice. "I wouldn't want to be irritating. Which is the precise reason—"

"You want to take a little boy to a shelter to sweat to death in the days ahead?"

"I do have places to go—"

"Not many people will be going anywhere today, Mrs. Wells. They're begging people to stay off the streets. I'm willing to bet that it's impossible to get through half of them. In fact, I'm willing to bet it's impossible just to drive around the cul-de-sac right now."

"If I'm going to stay here," Katie said, "my name is Katie, or Katherine. Mrs. Wells gets irritating after a while."

He grinned, the anger suddenly gone. And when he smiled like that, he was very attractive. It was a sensual smile.

No wife. He had said so. But there had to be a woman somewhere in his life. Maybe lots of women.

Maybe he had so many of them he hadn't even noticed she was among the ranks.

Maybe she should quit speculating about the man.

Maybe she should keep doing so—she was contemplating staying in his house with her only child.

Ah, well. Surely, natural disasters made for strange bedfellows.

Not bedfellows. House fellows.

Oh, hell . . .

It seemed amazing that she knew some people fairly well and could still keep such a distance from them. And now here was this man she barely knew, and she was already thinking about such personal things as the look of his hands, the feel of his thigh against hers. She was tempted to stroke the contours of his cheek.

Chemistry. A certain draw, she told herself firmly. Almost animal instinct.

Thank God she was human, of course. She could feel such things and never act upon them.

Oh, God! But she was losing it.

"Katie," he said softly. "I would be delighted—no, I insist that you make my home your own. And as I've said, I'll be happy to leave, if you deem it necessary."

His voice was husky. Low. Masculine. As sensual as his smile.

Yes, leave. One of us needs to, she thought.

She was being an idiot.

"Fine," she said. "We'll stay—until we can leave, of course." She realized she was still hunched down, gathering up shoes. She was very close to him. She could inhale that very pleasant and subtle scent of man and soap and after-shave.

She stood quickly. "I'll put these upstairs, out of the way," she told him.

"Fine," he said.

Katie turned and ran up the stairs, opening a closet to dump the shoes.

The closet was empty.

Well, perhaps he didn't have a live-in girlfriend.

Idiot, Katie told herself. If he did have a live-in girlfriend, she'd probably be living in his room!

She slipped into Midge Holloway's loafers and found them a reasonable fit—the shoes were very narrow, which helped make them tighter. Now she was dressed—a borrowed bathrobe and borrowed shoes.

She came downstairs. Jordan still slept on the sofa.

Katie walked to the door and opened it. The rain had stopped again. The sky remained battleship gray, but the wind seemed to be dying down again.

Across the fallen trees in the center of the cul-de-sac, she could see her house very clearly. Suddenly, the urge to see exactly what was inside it was very strong.

She should find Drew Cunningham and tell him where she was going.

She should wake Jordan and tell him.

But when she walked to the sofa, her son was sleeping so peacefully that she didn't want to waken him. And Drew had disappeared somewhere.

And after all, she had agreed to stay here. She hadn't made him her lord and master or anything.

Her child was sleeping on his sofa.

But she was very confident of one thing. Jordan was certainly all right in the man's house.

She hurried to the door, promising herself that she would take a quick look and come right back.

She started across the street, noting that Drew Cunningham was right—you couldn't even drive a car around the cul-de-sac, there were so many trees down.

She walked—then climbed—her way across the street and came to her house.

The front door was banging open and shut in what remained of the wind.

She stepped into her living room. The carpeting squished beneath her feet—there was a good inch of water in it.

Midge's shoes were ruined. She made a mental note to replace her neighbor's shoes with a new pair Midge would love.

Then she looked around.

Her furniture was soaked, and bits of plaster lay all about. In the hallway, the whole of the roof was down.

She walked into the living room and threw off one of the curtains that had landed on the edge of the sofa. She inhaled, startled to find one of her cameras—dry, untouched by the water and wind because the drapery had somehow managed to fall and protect it.

She checked quickly. High-speed film, perfect for the gray day. And thirty exposures left.

She started to set the camera down, then slipped the strap over her shoulder. She wasn't leaving this camera now—not for a second. She wasn't going to take any chances.

At least she could capture something of today.

She turned, anxious, still checking.

If she wanted to capture a piece of Andrew, she could start right here. Her beautiful draperies were sodden, discolored lumps on the floor. Curtain rods hung in disarray. Her chairs were soaked and battered; a large croton bush—dirt and roots included— had slammed against her coffee table. Glass was everywhere. The living room was demolished.

And yet...

Strange things had remained. The camera on the couch had been just fine. And across the room, she could see a little rosewood wall stand that contained some of her small porcelain miniatures.

Not one of them had even moved.

And there, just down the wall from the stand...

She hurried across the living room, amazed to discover that the picture of her and Terry and Jordan as a three-year-old still hung in place.

The windows were gone, the roof was half caved in, and still... Her picture remained. It was so strange. In the midst of such destruction, strange and somewhat delicate things remained. She started to reach for the picture.

"Katie! What in God's name do you think you're doing!"

Stunned, she spun around. Drew Cunningham was standing in her doorway, hands on his hips, his voice that of a shipmaster yelling at a second mate.

"It's my house!" she said indignantly.

"It's not safe!" he exploded.

"I have to—"

"Katie, look up, look out!"

"The storm is over—" Katie began, but looked up as he had warned her. She could already hear a strange, tearing sound. As she stared at the ceiling, Drew came hurtling across the room, throwing his arms around her and himself upon her as he brought them both down to the floor away from the wall.

She was beneath him. And even as they landed, a large chunk of plaster came crashing down, the bulk of it missing them, but a corner of it breaking away and landing with a startling thud right on his back.

"Oh!" Katie gasped in alarm.

He raised his shoulders quickly without a word or a groan, and the plaster fell to his side. He remained above Katie, and she met his eyes, shaking.

She struggled quickly for words. "I'm sorry, are you all right—?"

"I'm all right."

"You're covered with plaster."

"I said I'm all right!"

She might have been killed. He might have been killed. And it would have been her fault for running in here. But the shakes were dwindling to something an awful lot like warm, shooting tremors.

And she wasn't at all sure the feeling was coming from the danger of the storm-damaged house.

All she really knew was that he was half lying atop her, that she could feel the heady fever of his body, the shape and form of it, the warmth and life of the muscles in his thighs and chest . . .

"Dammit, Katie—"

"I said I was sorry!"

"You can get killed running into dangerous places like this without knowing what the condition is!"

"You could have been killed, as well!"

"I, at least, know what the hell I'm doing!"

"But it's my house!"

For a moment, he looked as if he would shout at her again, and she was ready, tense and ready. Somehow, she was afraid to lose this argument, and if she just kept shouting back, she'd be all right.

But he didn't shout at her again. He opened his mouth, then fell silent. Then he said softly, "Katie, it's not safe."

It wasn't safe. Not at all.

And she wasn't thinking of her house...

Chapter 4

The immediate danger didn't last long.

Before many more seconds had ticked by, they were interrupted by a tentative call from outside the house.

"Mom? Mr. Cunningham?"

"Jordan!" Katie cried. She set her hands on Drew's chest to push him away, but he was already up, reaching down a hand to help her up, too.

They were both somewhat whitened by ceiling plaster, and Katie wasn't sure whether to laugh or try to apologize again. Before she could do either, her camera swung around from her shoulder and belted him in the ribs.

He grunted.

"What now—?"

"Sorry!" she said again.

"You came in here for a camera?"

"I came in here to see what was left!"

"And you picked up a camera?"

She gritted her teeth. "I'm a photographer. Free lance. It's what I do for a living."

"But—"

"And I'm good at it and I don't have a house anymore and I might need what I can make off of storm pictures! Not to mention the fact that this has been something that should be remembered!"

"It's still not worth your life!" he told her.

Of course not. But before she could assure him that she hadn't meant to put anyone in danger, including herself, she heard her son calling to her again. "Mom? Mr. Cunningham? Are you in there?"

"Yes!" Katie called quickly. "Don't come in, I'll come out."

"Mr. Cunningham needs to come, too. There's a lady on the phone for him. Can you believe it? We've barely got a house and Mr. Cunningham's phone is still working!"

Drew grimaced, then set his hands on Katie's shoulders, spinning her around and urging her toward the door, which was hanging open.

She felt his hands on her shoulders as they walked.

There was a lady on the phone for him. Well, of course, he hadn't been spending his life in celibacy, waiting for her.

Katie was startled by the strength of the jealousy that seemed to pour through her.

Drew propelled her out of the house. Jordan stood on the porch, watching them with open curiosity. "I was trying to see what was left," Katie told her son. "Mr. Cunningham stopped me."

"The place isn't safe," Drew said. The words were quiet. The tension in his voice was nearly controlled.

Jordan sighed. "Anyone can see that, Mom."

Drew Cunningham was behind her. She was certain that he was nodding sagely at the wisdom of a ten-year-old—a child brighter than his mother.

"Yes," she murmured, just a little acidly, "Mr. Cunningham has so informed me." She spun around. "Don't you think you should run over and answer your phone, Drew?"

"Oh, yeah, the lady is real worried," Jordan said. "I told her that you were fine, that you'd gone out to chase my mom somewhere. She was real nice, so I told her that your house was just fine, and she wasn't quite sure who I was so I tried to explain that our house wasn't fine. I think I confused her worse."

"Maybe you'd better hurry," Katie suggested sweetly.

"And I think you'd better follow along with me," he said, not seeming to be in a hurry to rectify things. "It's not safe to go into that house."

"But—"

"I know you want to see what you can salvage. If you'll just wait a few minutes and come with me now, I'll come back with you and make sure that you sift through the house safely."

"How come you can be safe and I can't?" Kate asked.

"Because I'm an architect and a builder," he said flatly. Well, that explained why he had managed to be there every day when they had been working on his house.

And it would certainly explain how his had stood when hers had not.

He was watching her digest the information. But he didn't say anything else to her.

"Jordan, get your mom. Come on."

Jordan seemed to like the man, who could be downright irritating, Katie decided. "Mom, come on."

Right. Just what she wanted to do. Walk to Drew's house and listen to him explain to some mystery woman that he had been saddled with a thirty-something woman and her child since the storm.

She gritted her teeth. All right. She'd stand right in front of him and make him just as uncomfortable as she could while he made his explanations.

She followed him to his house but stood in the foyer as he went in. He answered the phone on the cherry-wood table next to the sofa. He had to know she had come in behind him, but he didn't seem uncomfortable in the least. Katie could hear every word he had to say.

"Hi! Yes, I'm fine, and this place is fine, but the development isn't so fine." He was silent for a moment. "By God, I swear, I don't know, but I will find out." A few minutes later, he said, "Something went very wrong. I haven't had a chance to see quite what yet . . . I have the little battery television. We've seen a lot. We—yes, I have a neighbor and her son here. Her house caved in. Three of them came down, four of them stood just fine.'' The woman talked again, and he listened, sitting on the sofa, heedless of the plaster that covered him. He rubbed his temples. "I will find out. Someone was falling off somewhere," he said. Katie felt herself shiver at the threat in his words. She wondered what he was going to find out—and she was suddenly glad she wasn't the someone who had been falling off somewhere.

The woman talked for a few more minutes, then Drew assured her that though the electricity was gone, everything else was okay. She must have told him she loved him, because he said, "Love you, too," then hung up. He sat there thoughtfully for a few minutes, and neither Katie nor Jordan moved.

Then he stared across the living room at them, as if just remembering that they were there.

The battery-operated television was still on, and with the room so quiet, they could hear the news again. More reports were coming in. It was becoming obvious that Broward County had fared well, that even North Miami and downtown Miami itself had survived the storm well enough. The destruction had started in the Coral Gables area, moved southward and had become devastating.

Homestead Air Force Base had been damaged. The reporter said that for mile after endless mile from the Falls area all the way down to Homestead, there was destruction. People were beginning to wander around. They were warned to stay off the roads. They were advised about shelters. They were alerted about office buildings and stores that no longer existed.

Listening, Katie found herself moving into the living room with Jordan next to her like a second skin.

The three of them were staring at the little television.

She hadn't realized that half of her county lay in the same condition as her home. Perhaps it wasn't so strange that her house had fallen—it was stranger that Andrew Cunningham's had stood.

As they watched in silent horror, more and more of the destruction began to unfold. The National Guard was arriving in places hardest hit. Although the tower had blown off the National Hurricane Center in Coral Gables, the downtown area had sustained the storm well. The homes in Gables Estates had taken a beating, and people were already calling Gables-By-The-Sea Gables-Beneath-The-Sea. Still, it was becoming apparent that hardest hit had been Naranja, Goulds, Homestead and Cutler Ridge, with the Falls area— their area—taking a massive strike as well.

The television crews were out, skirting the devastation, the uprooted trees, the downed power lines. Estimates were pouring in. Tens of thousands of people were homeless. Boats had been swept incredible distances onto the shore—and right into houses.

Officials worried about the death toll, about digging beneath the crumpled houses. Again, they warned people to be careful of downed wires, to drive

with caution when they did begin to drive again. They
advised people not to make calls if they didn't have to,
but of course, such advice was ludicrous, for everyone had family.

"Oh, God! My father!" Katie exclaimed.

Drew Cunningham's brooding attention was drawn
to her. He picked up his phone, set it against his ear,
heard a dial tone and handed it to Katie.

"They just said not to call—"

"Make it fast, then. Just tell him that you're okay."

"You don't know my father. He called at three
a.m.—right before the world exploded. And it's long
distance—"

"Mom, it's a natural disaster!" Jordan chimed in.
"I'm sure Mr. Cunningham will let you pay him for
the call later!"

Drew Cunningham grinned. "I'll just charge inter-
est. Call him quickly. We don't know how long the
phone will last."

Katie dialed, then said, "Hi, Dad!" as cheerfully as
she could the moment her father answered the phone.

She had to pull the phone away from her ear—Ron
Wheeler spoke with such passion. "Katie! I've been
worried sick! What's happened, where are you? Are
you okay, is my grandson okay? I've been seeing the
pictures on television—my God, Katie, where are
you?"

"I'm across the street at a neighbor's. I'm fine,
Jordan is fine. I just called to tell you that."

"Then your house—"

"My house is damaged, yes."

"I told you that you should have come up here!" Ron insisted. She knew he was worried, but he also seemed to be forgetting that she was not only over twenty-one, but a few months past thirty-one, as well.

And he was speaking loudly enough to be heard in the next state, she was certain.

"Dad, the phones aren't lasting well. I just wanted to say that I'm fine—"

"I'm coming down."

"Don't come down, Dad! There's nowhere to stay."

"Then you get yourself right up here."

"Dad, I can't come right away, I have to see about my home, my—my life!"

She glanced at Drew Cunningham. He was watching her with a certain amount of amusement.

"Have to go now, Dad. I'll call again soon. I'm fine, and I can't leave right away. When I can come up there, I will."

She didn't wait. Ron Wheeler started to say something else.

"Bye, Dad! Take care!" she said swiftly, drowning out whatever he might have had to say. Then she handed the phone quickly to Drew, and he set it in its cradle.

"Any other calls?" Drew asked. He was looking at Jordan.

"My dad is dead," Jordan said, and Katie realized her son had intuitively known that Drew was suggesting Katie should let Jordan's father know they were all right, if she was divorced.

"Oh, I'm sorry," Drew said softly.

"It's all right. It's been a long time now," Jordan said, but he stood up, straightening his shoulders beneath the too big robe, and asked, "Can I go outside? In the front?"

"Sure," Katie said. "I'm coming myself. I want to get some pictures. The house—that poor banyan tree."

Jordan nodded and left them. Katie felt Drew's eyes on her. She wasn't sure why, but she felt a flush coming to her cheeks.

She turned to look at him. His gold eyes were intense as he watched her. "I should have known," he said. "I'm sorry."

"You should have known what?" Katie asked.

"That your husband had passed away."

"Why should you have known?"

He grinned suddenly. "The way your father talked to you. He's a man who still feels he has the responsibility to look after you. That usually comes when a woman—is alone."

Katie felt her flush deepen, and she looked down at her hands. He laughed softly, and she looked at him quickly. "He hasn't realized yet that I'm capable of looking after myself and that I don't mind being alone. But then—" she shrugged "—my mother has been gone a while now, too, so I suppose I'm good for him, too. He really is a great guy."

"I imagine," Drew said. "What happened?"

"To what?"

"To your husband."

"Oh," Katie said softly. It had been a long time. Over five years. She had learned to cherish all her memories, and just a hint of sadness filled her when she thought about Terry, though she could still grow angry at the way he had died. "A drunk driver," she told Drew.

"I'm very sorry."

"So am I. He was twenty-seven years old. It was an incredible waste of life."

She rose swiftly, not wanting his pity and certainly not needing it.

She had her father to worry about her, after all.

"I'm going to take pictures now," she told him. "while everything is still... awful."

"It's going to be awful for a long time," he told her softly.

She nodded. "I know that. But still..." She shrugged, lifting her hands. "It's what I do."

He stood, as well. "Just be careful."

"My father already told me that."

"No matter what your father has seen on television, I'm sure he hasn't seen the half of it. Be careful."

"Yes, sir!" she promised, and turned toward the door. She realized that he was following her. She paused, turning back questioningly.

"I know I'm not going to be able to keep you out of your house forever," he told her. "I'm going to go over and see how stable the structure is—and what happened to the roof."

"But it's not safe—"

"I know what to watch out for. And like I said, I know I won't be able to keep you away forever, right?"

She met the golden gleam in his eyes and smiled. He created the strangest emotions within her. One minute she was annoyed, another irritated—he could treat her just like a child. Then the next minute she was feeling anything but childlike, with little lightning flashes of heat racing through her at his lightest touch or softest word. She was doing things she just never did.

Thinking about him . . .

Imagining him . . . naked.

Katie, get a grip!

She turned staunchly and started out of the house, speaking quickly to cover her confusion. "You've got to understand—I have to get into the house. I have to see if I have any clothing left! Any pictures, anything of Jordan's, anything at all."

"I do understand," he told her quietly. "And that's why I'll get in there now and see what's up." He reached out suddenly and wiped gently at her cheek with his thumb.

"Plaster," he told her.

"You're still wearing a lot yourself."

He shrugged. "But I might soon be wearing more."

"And I really haven't anything else to wear, period!" Katie said, laughing. "So for the moment, I'm not so sure it matters."

She grinned, turned and went out the door, lifting her camera and staring through the lens at the havoc created by the storm.

The banyan first, she thought. It hadn't been a person or an animal, but it had been alive. For years and years. It had shaded them, sheltered them, been a haven for squirrels and possums and birds.

It clearly denoted the power of the storm, for when it had come up, it had taken with it concrete and earth. It was amazing to see it ripped from the ground.

She quickly became involved with her work, taking care—she didn't have nearly enough film. She needed rolls and rolls of it. Jordan saw her as she worked, and came to stand quietly behind her, pointing out sad features caused by the storm.

There was a torn teddy bear stuck in one of the branches of the tree.

Katie snapped several pictures.

She turned to the outside of her house then, coming around the rear. The screen enclosure had completely unfolded and lay in her muddied pool. The steel beams had buckled.

She began to snap more pictures.

Jordan paused over a dead, almost featherless bird. She snapped more pictures, feeling as if a little piece of her heart tore out as she did so.

The occasional whip of wind came less and less. The sky began to clear.

The sun began to get hot.

She ran out of film.

She stopped with Jordan, sinking down to her lawn, watching as some of her neighbors started moving about, as well. Brandon Holloway, lifting palms from his front porch, waved to her.

She waved back.

A few minutes later, Drew Cunningham came out of her house.

"You should be all right now to do a little exploring inside. I pulled down what was about to fall, and the rest of the structure seems to be okay." He hesitated, seeming worried and confused—and angry. "The structure is still good. The walls are solid inside as well as out. Your windows are blown in, of course... but the house can be fixed. If you want it fixed."

"If I want it fixed?" she repeated blankly.

"You're insured, right?"

"Right."

He shrugged. "Eventually, the insurance adjusters will make it around—probably after the looters, of course, but, when they come, you'll surely be offered a settlement. You could bail out and move."

Katie shook her head. "I don't want to move. Jordan loves his school. I've lived near here all my life. I can remember when this was all swampland. I have no desire to move."

"Good," he said softly, and the golden glitter was in his eyes again. "Then I promise you it can be fixed. I'll see you at my house in a while. I want to look at the other houses that went down and see if I can do anything for anyone else for the moment. Then I've got to make some calls. When you get what you want from the house, just bring it over. I'll help you two get settled for the next few days. Or weeks,'' he corrected himself, staring at her house.

"Fine. Thanks," Katie said lightly.

He left her and walked across the road, hailing Brandon Holloway. There was a big palm down in the middle of the road. Brandon helped Drew drag the downed tree off the street. She could hear them shouting to each other as they cleared the street of palms and debris.

"Want to try the house, Mom? Or maybe we should go help them clear the street."

Katie shrugged, rising from her devastated lawn. "Maybe we'd better see if we have any clothes left at all, huh? We'll start losing these robes if we get carried away."

Jordan grinned.

"And then everyone would laugh!" Katie warned him.

"They may laugh, and they may just go, 'Hubba, hubba!'" her son informed her.

She tousled his hair. "At me? Or you?"

"Mom! I'm a kid. At you."

"Thanks for the vote of confidence. But then again, they may just laugh. Let's go see if we can't find some clothing."

She started for the house, Jordan behind her. She warned him to be very careful of all the broken glass. Once they were in, she started to salvage the pictures that had survived in the living room. When they were piled up, Jordan left her and went to what remained of his room.

She went to hers.

It was so strange. The windows were caved in on her elegant bath. The tub was filled with mud.

The medicine chest above the commode—which carried a dead bird—hadn't been touched. She opened it and scooped the things they would need most into a little bag—Band-Aids, aspirin, antiseptic, toothpaste and toothbrushes.

She still had room, so she added some makeup, then some more. She had lost a great deal, but there were also pockets in her home where things had barely been touched.

Drew Cunningham was going to start to think that she was planning on moving in permanently.

A minute later, Jordan came hurrying into her room. "Mom! All my drawers are just fine, can you believe it. My Star Wars collection is fine, and my baseball cards aren't even damp!"

"That's great!" Katie said with forced enthusiasm. Then she lifted a brow. "How about clothing, Jordan? Have you got any of that?"

"Jean, shorts, T-shirt. The drawers were fine. The closet is soaked. The plaster is all caving in there."

"Grab some sneakers out of it anyway. We'll have to find some way to rinse them out for you to wear until we can buy some. If and when we find a store that can open!" she added.

"Right. I have a duffel bag. Should I pack it?"

"Yep, sounds good."

Jordan left her. She started to dig through her belongings.

Her nightstand had been whipped across the room. Her drawers—the top one odds and ends, the bottom one underwear—had broken out, and her books and notes, pens, papers, calendar and letters were all in wet muddy piles near the closet.

Undies, bras, slips and camisoles were strewn about, a negligee on the lamp on her main dresser, several pairs of panties at the foot of the bed. She squished through the carpeting in Midge's loafers and tried to collect what pieces were dry and in good shape.

She was just reaching for a black bra that hung on her downed curtain rod when she heard a throat being cleared.

Drew Cunningham was back. Looking absurdly handsome for a damp man covered in plaster and palm fronds, he grinned, his fingers on a pair of red silk panties. He tossed them across the room to Katie. "Those look good."

She caught them.

"Are you done helping humanity already?" she asked him.

He sobered, the amusement in his eyes quickly gone. "Humanity, here, won't be helped for a long time. We've cleared the circle—it can be driven now, though I don't know what's beyond it. I've made some calls, and we'll have trucks out here tomorrow to start hauling away some of the heavy refuse. Florida Power and Light has already been out working, and aid seems to be pouring in from all over. But if you haven't noticed, it's almost dark. And we're under a curfew—most of the businesses down south on the highway were destroyed, and the thieves moved in right away. Perhaps you haven't noticed, but you haven't eaten all day.''

Eaten! She hadn't even had a drink. And she had a little boy. One who hadn't complained once today about anything.

"Aren't you thirsty?" Drew asked her. He smiled again, slipping a beige camisole from the corner of a broken drawer and tossed it to her.

She caught the camisole, staring at him, realizing that her throat was very dry and that her stomach was rumbling.

She calmly folded the camisole and added it to her stack of things. "What are you suggesting?" she asked sweetly. "Should we send out for pizza?"

"No, we need to go to my house and cook some food that is quickly unfreezing," he told her. He shrugged. "Well, we'll have some nice room-temperature red wine to go with our steaks and Spaghettios!"

She found herself smiling, even when he discovered a forest green wraparound nightgown, sheer, soft and still silky. She started to take it from him. He held tight for a moment.

"Pretty piece," he teased.

She swept it from his hand. "Thanks."

"Is that all you've managed to salvage?" he asked, looking at the pile of undergarments on her bed. "If so, you're going to make for an interesting neighbor. Housemate, actually."

"Oh, I don't know," she managed to say smoothly. "You do seem to be a connoisseur, so I imagine that you've had your fair share of women walking around in such garments."

He smiled, shrugged and lifted his hands. "Just what is a fair share?" he asked.

More than I've had, Katie thought, but she was determined she could play this sexual game casually and with nonchalance.

"More than you probably deserve," she assured him.

"How do you know what I deserve?"

"I'm just thinking about that poor lovely woman who was so concerned about you earlier today. Remember her? When she finished speaking to you, I distinctly heard you say, 'I love you, too.'"

"Hmm. You do pay attention," he told her.

She shrugged, trying to make a neat pile of her things. "I didn't have much choice. You more or less dragged me back across the street."

"I protest. I didn't lay a hand on you."

"I protest. You most certainly did."

"Only in the house. This house. And only to try to keep you from getting hurt."

"You were—most noble," she assured him quickly. "And still," she murmured, feeling a flush coming to her cheeks again, no matter what her determinations, "I'm wondering if I ought to be sleeping in the Holloways' weight room."

"Jordan can have his own room at my house with a Nintendo and the works," he reminded her. Serious again, he added, "And I told you. If you're uncomfortable, I can go somewhere else."

"Don't be absurd. I couldn't let you leave your home."

"Oh, but you could," he said, and he sounded weary and somewhat bitter again.

"All right," she said frowning. "I wouldn't. But I would appreciate it if you would refrain—"

"From handling your clothing?"

She sighed. "Would you see if I have anything decent in my closet?" she asked him.

The door had blown away. He stepped into the huge walk-in closet, then stepped out.

"Half and half," he told her. "North wall drenched, south wall all right. Your suitcases are a disaster. Got any garbage bags?"

"Yes. Well, I did. If they didn't blow away."

Jordan had come to the door. "I'll try the kitchen!" he offered cheerfully.

A moment later, he was back. The toaster was gone, so was the coffee machine. But the paper plates, cups, napkins and garbage bags were just fine.

The three of them set to work packing her things to take them over to Drew's. Katie's stomach began to grumble. "We should give this up for now."

"In a minute," Drew told her. "It could rain again," he explained when she looked at him. "Let's get what we can."

They did, making several trips across the circle. The Holloways saw them and came out to help.

Darkness had fallen when they finished. They bid the Holloways good-night, then started lighting candles in Drew's living room.

He produced a gallon jug of water that they half emptied almost immediately.

When everyone's thirst was slaked, Drew looked at Katie across the rim of the water bottle. "It really is steak and Spaghettios. Want to turn the meat over the Sterno or check out the refrigerator for vegetables and fruit?"

"I'll take the steaks," Katie said.

They moved into the kitchen, bringing the little television with them. They were in the middle of the disaster, and naturally, they were interested in every word about the storm and its aftermath.

Katie got the Sterno going on the corner of the island in the kitchen. The house was beautifully designed, with more custom touches than her own. The kitchen was equipped with everything from a subzero freezer to wonderful cherry and glass built-in cabinets. Though the kitchen was expansive, it seemed very warm and intimate in the candlelight.

Jordan set the table, Drew made a salad. He hadn't lost his water, but he used bottled water to wash the lettuce. The news reporter had warned that the water had been contaminated.

"At least it will be fine to shower in," Drew murmured.

"And we do need showers again," Katie agreed. Maybe they should have showered first—they were both a bit wild looking, half damp, half plastered. But by now, hunger was the driving force.

"Cold showers," Drew said.

"Cold will feel great!" Jordan told them. "It's starting to get awfully hot!"

"It's going to get hotter in the days to come," Drew said. "The temperature will rise, once all the wind and cloud cover are completely gone."

Katie flipped the steaks over the Sterno. They seemed to be coming out amazingly well. In a few minutes she had them on plates.

And the Spaghettios were warmed through, as well.

"Ready on this end," she told Drew.

"Ready on this one, too," he told her.

In a few minutes, they were all seated at the small kitchen table. Drew had taken down the boards and opened the doors that had once led out to his patio.

The screen that had stood over his pool was in it, but the darkness covered the disaster, and the breeze that moved in was pleasantly cool. Drew had produced a vintage red wine, and they were drinking out of beautiful wineglasses.

Jordan was drinking warm Gatorade from one of the wineglasses, and he smiled all through dinner, as if he was having fun.

It was fun, Katie reflected. They had all worked well together. And it was warm and very comfortable to sit down together, to eat together, to comment on the warnings the television gave, to sit back wearily and realize that they had survived something more traumatic than they had realized at first.

"First night. The National Guard is in, the curfew is on." Drew lifted his wineglass toward the television where lights were streaming onto darkened streets to show damaged houses. Signs were already painted on those houses. *You loot, we shoot!* There was the very simple and profound, *Andrew sucks!*

"I could take that one personally," Drew murmured. Katie flashed him a smile.

"I imagine you might have some ribbing coming your way in the next few days," she told him.

He shrugged and poured her some more wine. She was certainly unwinding, feeling very relaxed. The steaks had been good, his salad had been simple but filling, and even the Spaghettios had tasted good. She was very tired and oddly content.

Especially considering she hadn't much of a house left. And practically no personal effects at all.

She had Jordan. And she had seen enough on television to realize just how many people had lost their homes, and just how many of them were now sleeping in the tent cities that had begun to spring up in the afternoon.

"I think we've lost Jordan," Drew commented softly.

Katie looked at her son. He had pushed his plate away, set his head down on the table and fallen asleep.

"Poor kid, he must have been really exhausted," Drew said.

"I'll bring him up, and then I'll come right back down to pick up the dishes."

"I'll take him up for you," Drew told her.

"But I—"

He was already standing, lifting Jordan. "You're very defensive, you know," he told Katie. "I'm bigger. It's easier for me to take him upstairs. Just say thanks and let me do it for you."

She had started to rise. She sank back, shrugging. "I'm not defensive!" she told him defensively. "I'm just—capable."

He smiled, picking up Jordan. "Very capable," he told her, and disappeared into the shadowy corridor, sliding a flashlight from the counter as he did so to guide his way up the stairs.

When he was gone, Katie started to clear the table. She scraped and rinsed the dishes quickly, and soaped them liberally since she had nothing but cold water to wash them in. She was just about finished when Drew came into the kitchen and leaned against the counter, picking up his wineglass and sipping at the inch of burgundy that remained.

"Tired?" he asked her.

"I hadn't thought about it until I saw Jordan crash into the table. But I am. Very."

He shrugged. "No one has slept in at least thirty-six hours. And those have been some hours."

She nodded, finishing the last of the dishes and wiping her hands on a towel. The kitchen suddenly seemed small. She barely knew him; she was staying with him. No, she couldn't say that she barely knew him. Perhaps she didn't know a whole lot about him, but in the hours they had been together, she thought she had come to know him. She felt as if she knew him ridiculously well.

"By the way, thank you," she said softly.

"For what?"

"Letting us stay here."

She didn't understand why, but the comment seemed to cause his jaw to tighten as if he was angry. His reply sounded angry, as well.

"You don't need to thank me."

"But—"

"Dammit, Katie, trust me. You don't owe me any thanks."

She turned around a little blindly, realizing that she was exhausted, that she still wanted to check on Jordan and that she needed a shower—a cold one, of course—before going to bed. She was so tired she couldn't really begin to make sense of anything— much less a man who was as much an enigma as Drew Cunningham.

"Well, then, I won't thank you," she said, walking from the kitchen toward the dark living room. "I'll say good-night. If it's all right, I'll take this flash-light."

"It's fine. And Katie . . ." His voice trailed away. Soft now. Sensual. Too sensual.

"Yes?"

"Thank you. Dinner was great."

She looked at him. He was grinning pleasantly, still leaning against the counter. She nodded. "Dinner was almost nice," she told him. "I haven't eaten by candlelight in a long time."

"Neither have I."

She remained there a moment, then found herself asking him, "My staying isn't going to create any difficulties for you?"

"Such as?" he asked.

She shrugged. "Well, with your friend on the phone today. The one you—love."

He set his wineglass down. "I think she'll deal with it. In fact, I think she'd have my head on a platter if I didn't see to it that you and Jordan had a place to stay."

"Oh?"

"Mom is like that," he said.

"Mom?"

"My mother, Katie."

"Oh." She found herself flushing. She'd definitely been nosy. And he had certainly managed to hold off from telling her for awhile.

But then, she had gotten an answer from him that she liked.

"Where is Mom?" she asked him.

"Boca Raton," he told her. "Where's Dad?"

She grinned. "Orlando."

"At least they're both safe and out of this," he said.

Katie nodded. "Yeah. Well...thanks again. Whether you want to hear it or not."

"Good night," he told her.

She took one of the big lantern flashlights from the counter and hurried up the stairs. She found Jordan in the room at the end of the hall, sleeping comfortably on a double bed. She kissed his forehead and left him.

She started to the guest room, then paused, seeing a half open door.

She pushed it open and discovered an office. There was a desk and a big drafting table and all manner of drawing supplies. She threw the flashlight over the room, too tired to really study it yet impressed with all she saw. There was a rendering of a house on the drafting table, and it was done in beautiful detail.

Her host was certainly talented.

And more...

She quickly left the room and hurried along the hall to her own. Luckily, she had piled all her things on the floor and not on the bed.

She closed the door, and walked straight into the bathroom, setting up the light so she could take a shower. She came out, wrapped up in a towel and searched through the remnants of her belongings until she found a simple white cotton nightgown.

She couldn't quite manage to slip into any of the silk he had teased her about. The world still seemed too uncertain to be dressed in anything that wasn't a little bit encompassing.

She was in a stranger's house.

No, she had decided he wasn't a stranger. She didn't know much about him, but she had seen how he managed in the middle of the storm, leaving safe shelter to save her and Jordan.

Clearing the roads.

Helping.

She wasn't worried about him. She was worried about herself. She was so tempted to leave her room again, to try to find him in the dark house, to...

To curl up beside him somewhere. Feel his arms around her. Holding her.

"Katherine Mary Wheeler Wells!" she admonished herself.

She'd been alone too long, or the storm had unhinged more than her house.

Sleep. She needed sleep.

She stretched out in his guest bed, so tired she was certain she would sleep instantly.

But she didn't. She listened, and wondered where he was.

Then she closed her eyes and began to drift to sleep. She felt pleasantly secure and glad to be in his house.

Dangerous, she decided.

But she was too tired to care.

She smiled before she dozed.

She should have been devastated. But she was comfortable, warm. And there still seemed to be a sweet touch of fever inside her. She was looking forward to the morning.

And finding out more—all that she could—about her attractive, sometimes kind, sometimes brooding, sometimes very angry and intense—

And always fascinating—

Host.

She opened her eyes just before she slept. "Thanks, God. For bringing us through. For keeping us safe."

She hesitated a second. "And for making that woman on the phone this morning his mother!"

And with that, she managed to turn, plump up her pillow and sleep very deeply and very well.

Chapter 5

She felt as if she were being awakened from the dead. She groaned as she felt her weary body shaken and she heard a voice calling her name coming from a great distance.

It wasn't coming from a great distance. There was a man standing over her bed, Andrew Cunningham. He had been whispering her name—now he was saying it louder and shaking her more firmly.

"Katie, we need to get anything out of your house that we can. I've got some roofers coming in an hour to at least do a patch job on the houses, so you won't be able to get back in today. And I can't stay very long here myself—I've got to go and see what's left of my office."

She'd been so sound asleep, but she bolted up, instantly awake. Her hair was wild; she was glad she'd chosen the encompassing cotton nightgown and she was suddenly wishing she could wake up like the stars in the soap operas—she knew she was completely tousled, disoriented and far less than glamorous.

But he was smiling at her. And she caught her breath as his fingers tenderly—briefly—caressed her cheek. "Katie, I'm sorry to wake you, but I thought that you'd want to do a little more exploring in there before you can't get in."

"I'm up," Katie said. "I'm awake. You—you have roofers coming out here already?"

"They'll just be doing patch jobs—that's about all anybody will be able to do for awhile. But it will help keep the rest of the house from becoming more destroyed than it is. Jordan is up—he's just waiting for you to go on over."

He turned and left her. Katie jumped up and rushed into the bathroom, hurriedly brushing her teeth, scrubbing her face and splashing it with cold water to wake herself up. She scrounged through her things until she found a pair of white shorts and a red tailored sleeveless cotton shirt—the coolest combination she could find—and dressed hurriedly. Even as she slipped on Midge Holloway's loafers once again, she heard a tapping on her door. Jordan was standing there, very carefully balancing a cup of black coffee.

"Drew—Mr. Cunningham—said that you might need this," Jordan told her.

"Thanks." She took the coffee and sipped it. It was very good. Drew Cunningham might not be a gourmet cook, but he made very good coffee and he seemed quite capable of taking care of himself. "I'll be right with you," she told Jordan, and took the coffee with her into the bathroom. She didn't want to get carried away or anything, certainly not under these circumstances, but she had salvaged a little makeup, so maybe she should use it. Jordan waited at the foot of her bed while she quickly put on base and gave her eyelashes a whisk and a promise with mascara. "Did you have yours?" she asked Jordan.

"My what?"

"Coffee?"

"Mom, you know I don't drink coffee!" he reminded her, and she sensed that he was grinning. "I did have hot chocolate—and a cold Pop Tart. It was good. This is neat in a way. It's almost like camping indoors. If I could only have Nintendo, as well!" he said with a sigh.

"You can always read a book," Katie said.

"Sure, Mom. I'll read a book. I imagine I'll read lots of them. They say it will be two weeks to several months before everyone starts to get electricity back."

"Ugh!" Katie said.

"School will be very late opening," he told her happily.

"Don't sound so smug. You'll lose half your holidays because of it."

"Oh!" He sounded very unhappy then.

"Sorry," Katie told him. "Maybe it won't be so many," she said as she came out of the bathroom. He was sitting at the foot of the bed. "Besides, when the roads are clearer and I've done whatever I can do about getting our things out and the house fixed, we can go up and visit with Grandpa for awhile. We can go to Universal Studios and Disney World and Sea World and play gooney golf and the whole bit. Before school starts. Sound fun?"

"Sure." But he didn't sound as enthused as he might have. He shrugged. "I don't mind staying here."

"Oh," Katie said softly. "But it isn't our home, Jordan."

"It's all right for now, right?" he said hopefully.

"Yeah, it's fine for now. But come on, let's start salvaging some things."

She rinsed her coffee cup in the kitchen. Drew was no longer in the house, but she quickly discovered why.

Men with trucks had made it into the cul-de-sac. They were the roofers, she quickly realized. Drew was directing them to take boxes he had already packed out to the street.

He seemed to know the men, and had an easy relationship with them, even as they moved quickly and efficiently to do as they were instructed. Drew saw Katie come walking over and waved a hand to her. "I took all the books out of your den, the tapes, the discs—and it seems your VCR is okay, so I took it, too. Your garage stood fine, and I think all your chemicals and photo equipment are in it. You might want to start there. By the way—there's a small bathroom in my garage. You're welcome to turn it into a darkroom if you want to take photos and develop them."

"My things in the garage are all okay?" Katie said, incredulous. What a wonderful break!

"Fine," he told her. "I've got to go. I'll see you all later. Giles there is the foreman on the job. He'll tell you when he needs you out."

Katie nodded and started to thank him. He was already gone, walking down the path to the cul-de-sac. He slipped behind the wheel of a car there, a bright red Ford Probe.

Jordan would just love the car, Katie thought.

"I'm going to see what he saved of my games in the den, Mom," Jordan told her. He hesitated. "And I'm going to see what's left of that box of photos in there."

She knew what he was looking for. She had done a special book for him—and herself—with some of the pictures she had taken of his father. It meant a lot to him.

"Maybe I should help you first."

"I'm fine—I can check myself. Get your camera stuff, Mom. It's important, too."

He wanted to be alone; she let him. She watched him walk into the house while she entered the garage.

Her car, a dated BMW, was fine, as were the shelves around the edges. Even her washer and dryer seemed all right. Funny, but yesterday she had only seen what had been destroyed. Today she was seeing what had not.

She set to work gathering her equipment, then thankfully finding that she had more of her own and Jordan's clothing in the dryer. She had just finished putting everything in her car to drive it across the street when one of the roofers, the one called Giles, walked into the garage. "Can I give you a hand here with anything? We need to get started."

"I'm fine, thanks," Katie told him.

"We just took your son back across the street with his boxes."

"Thank you. That was really nice."

Another of the roofers had come in. He and Giles were both tall. Giles was in his mid-forties, the other was younger with white-blond hair and a quick, engaging smile. He nodded to Katie.

"You guys are back to work fast!" Katie said.

Giles shrugged. "We're roofers. We'll be working hard and fast for months now. I don't think there's a roof between Homestead and Broward County that didn't suffer some damage."

"How did you make out yourselves?" Katie asked them.

"I'm living in the office," Giles told her.

"I'm his roommate," the younger man said, still grinning. "And mind you, even the office had damage."

"This was really bad, huh?" Katie said.

The older man shrugged. "Yeah, it was bad. But actually, I always knew my place wasn't put together quite right. It was just nice looking, and I could afford it. I always meant to put a new roof on it myself, but... well, you know. These houses, though, they should have all stood. Like Mr. Cunningham's. Glass damage, yes, but not this."

"There are staples here," the younger man said.

Katie frowned. "Staples? On a roof?"

"Oh, yeah, and it's legal, and sometimes the staples even hold real well and only shingles might rip away. It's just that Hunnicunn doesn't usually use staples. The roofs on these homes are usually built the old-fashioned way, tongue in groove, sturdy, solid. The house would have to blow away for the roof to come off—even in a big wind like Andrew. Well, we'd better get to work. Oh—by the way, we're going to rip out your soaked carpet. There's no way to dry it, and the smell will get really bad in a couple of days."

"That's really nice of you. You're roofers. It isn't necessary."

"Mr. Cunningham wants this place taken care of."

"I'd do it just for you!" the younger man said.

Katie grinned. He was a flirt. Cute. "Thanks," she told him. "I'll just get out of your way now."

She drove the BMW across the street. She went into the house and discovered that Jordan had acquired all manner of boxes—the roofers had brought them—and that his boxes were strewn all over the living room.

"Jordan, we've got to do something with all this. We aren't in our—"

"Our own house, I know," he told her, grinning. "I'll get it all picked up. Honest, Mom."

"Did you find the book?" she asked him.

"Yeah. It's half okay and half not."

"I think I had most of the negatives in the garage," Katie told him, and saw the light of hope in his eyes. "Mr. Cunningham said that I could make a darkroom out of the bathroom in his garage. After we pick up, I'm going to see what I can do out there."

"Pick up, right," Jordan said wearily. "Okay!"

The hours ticked by as they went to work. She listened to the reports of how Andrew had swept across the southern tip of Florida, then gained momentum again to slam into Louisiana.

By the afternoon, the sun had come up in a big way. It was August in Florida.

Killer hot.

She and Jordan rested, going out back to stare at the destroyed pool and to catch what they could of the breeze. They rested awhile, then she started on her crude darkroom. She developed the pictures she had taken the first day, and was pleased with them. She needed to start getting them out to newspapers and magazines. She needed to take more pictures.

Tomorrow. She'd venture out.

Drew returned after dark and instantly excused himself to take a cold shower. Traffic had been a disaster, he told her briefly. It had felt good to get into his car to use the air-conditioning, but then he'd gotten into a gridlock, and he'd had to turn it off.

Twenty minutes later, he was back downstairs. He'd had plenty of ice in a cooler yesterday that had kept most of his meat, but the ice was nearly melted now, and so Katie had cooked the hamburger meat, which had looked as if it was defrosting the fastest. Drew seemed pleased to find dinner ready. "I just didn't think to eat today," he told her. "I'm starving. Spaghettios again?"

"Baked beans and canned pineapple and the rest of your lettuce and cucumbers. You do still have quite a supply of Spaghettios."

"I took whatever I could off the shelves Sunday morning," he told her, grimacing. "The grocery store was almost as deadly as the storm that morning!"

Katie smiled. She'd shopped Sunday herself. She had to agree. "Shall we eat?"

They had dinner. Jordan talked enthusiastically about the roofers. Drew asked about Katie's darkroom, and she told him she'd already developed pictures. Jordan retrieved the pictures, and Drew studied them by lamplight. His hazel-gold eyes touched hers across the table. "They're good. Very good."

"Thanks. I'm going to drive out tomorrow."

"Driving is hard."

Katie smiled. "I'm a good driver."

"Katie, the best driver in the world is in danger out there now."

"I have to get out," she told him.

"Maybe I can take you a few places."

"I am a big girl."

"Ah, but you see, I know where to take you. There's a hotel over by the water that was ripped to shreds—but some of the kids who had been staying in it were catching fish right out of the parking lot. There's a church up on Kendall that's been sliced almost right in half. There's mile after mile of blown-out shops. I know where to bring you.''

"But do you have the patience to wait with her?" Jordan asked, his eyes rolling.

Katie made a face at her son.

"How was your office?" Katie asked Drew.

"Damaged. But we were adding on when the storm struck. Most of the important areas came through with flying colors. We had good storm shutters and didn't even lose windows. The part that was being worked on is a mess, but compared to what else is out there, we're in great shape.''

"You did well," Katie said. "With your home, with your office."

"I went through a few hurricanes as a kid. Too much of our population down here didn't know what to expect. And Andrew was a fierce reminder of the power of the elements after all those years when this area was spared the brunt of the storms."

"Definitely," Katie agreed. She smiled. "But I thought I knew what I was doing, too. I had Sterno, batteries, flashlights and candles. I had water everywhere."

Andrew stood up suddenly, taking his plate to the sink. "Everything that you've lost will be replaced," he said, and she sensed an undercurrent of anger in his voice once again.

Perhaps he had thought she was complaining, when so many others were in worse shape, when she had heard so many tragic stories during the day. The death toll from the storm was rising, from heart attacks suffered by the elderly to the heart-wrenching instance of the unborn child that had died with its mother when she had a cerebral hemorrhage, unable to get medical attention.

She had nothing to complain about. She had Jordan, she had herself.

"I didn't mean to sound—"

"You didn't sound anything, Katie," he said, still angry.

She fell silent.

Jordan picked up his dish. "Anyone want to play Scrabble?" he asked hopefully.

Katie stayed silent.

Drew turned around, leaning against the counter. "If your mom is willing, so am I," Drew told him, looking at Katie. It was an apology of some kind.

"You don't have to play," Katie told him.

"I love Scrabble. I'll beat the pants off you both," he assured her.

She found herself grinning.

He did win, but only by a few points. When they finished the game, Jordan was yawning.

"You'd better get to bed," Katie told him.

"Why? Do I have to get up early?" he asked.

"If you want to come on a photo expedition, you do," Drew told him.

Jordan leaped right up. "You really want to take Mom around?"

"Yeah. I have to go by work, too, and I need to see to a few more things around here, but at least I can start out with you all. And show you what I know would make for good photos. Some things that shouldn't be forgotten.''

"Great!" Jordan started from the living room for the stairs. Then he came back. He shook Drew's hand and kissed Katie's cheek.

A moment later, Jordan was gone. Katie studied Drew in the candlelight where he sat across the coffee table from her. "You really don't have to take me around—"

"I want to."

"But it seems as if you feel that you're responsible for me. I really am very capable—"

"I know that. But I can't tell you just how bad things are. I stood in line for an hour and half today for ice and they ran out before they got to me. There aren't any stores left in this area—I had to ride along north just to find places that had managed to open."

"But this is when I need to take pictures," Katie said. "Before things are back to normal."

He leaned toward her. "Katie, things may never be back to normal," he told her softly.

"I need to get out now."

"Then you'll get out now," he told her. "It's not that people aren't going out—it's just that they aren't going out more than is necessary."

"Is there anyone helping with traffic?"

"Oh, yes, the police are out full force and the National Guard is doing a fantastic job. But the scope of the destruction..." His voice trailed away. "It's amazing." He was quiet for a moment. "Want to play another game of Scrabble?" he asked her.

She shook her head. "No, you beat me. Fair and square. I'm not in a thinking mode at the moment."

"Want to see a movie?"

"Is this an imagination test?"

He shook his head. "No, that little television has a tape player, as well."

"What have you got?" she asked him.

"Take a flashlight up to Jordan's room. I'll watch anything you find up there," he told her.

She went upstairs. She thought Jordan was sleeping, but he moved on the bed, then sat up.

"Sorry, I didn't mean to wake you."

"Mom? What are you doing?"

"Looking for a movie."

"A movie?"

"The television is a tape player, too."

"Oh. Hey, he's got lots of neat stuff. All of the *Alien* movies. The complete *Star Wars*. Horror movies—*The Raven*. That's great. Vincent Price was really neat."

"He still is," Katie murmured. Drew Cunningham certainly did have quite a selection. One whole corner of the bookshelves was taken up by stacks of tapes. Horror, sci-fi, action-adventure, Shakespeare, romance.

She decided at last on *Arsenic and Old Lace*.

She turned around. Jordan shrugged at her choice. "It's one of my favorites," she told him.

"It's not all that romantic," he told her.

Katie paused. "It was supposed to be?"

Jordan innocently lay down. "Hey, Mom. Watch whatever you want."

She kissed his forehead. "I will. Sleep tight."

"You, too," he told her. "And don't stay up too late, remember, you've got a busy day tomorrow."

"Yes, sir!" she told him.

She carried her movie downstairs. Drew did seem to like her choice. "One of my favorites," he said, slipping it into the slot on the small television. "It's not exactly wide screen or letter box," he apologized.

"It's a great movie," she said, "without any enhancement. Besides—it's a break from the storm."

He didn't argue that. "There's no popcorn," he said after a moment. "Well, I could build a fire and we could pop some, but we'd die of the heat."

"I can live without the popcorn."

"Want some lukewarm once-iced tea?" he asked.

"I'll get it."

"And we do have chips," he called.

It was really an amazing night. They set the bowl of chips between them and munched away, sipping the tea. They talked about Cary Grant and tried to recall all his movies. They lamented his loss, and they laughed at Peter Lorre. They sat close on the sofa, only the bowl of chips between them.

Then the movie ended, and the room seemed filled with silence.

"I'll pick this up—" Katie began.

"No, I will. Go to bed. You're hard to get up in the morning."

"I am not!"

"You were this morning."

"I was very tried."

"Then go get some more sleep now," he told her.

Katie nodded. "Good night," she told him. She paused. "Thank you again."

"Katie, do me two favors. Quit picking up, and quit thanking me."

"But—"

"I owe you, believe me."

"What do you mean by that?"

"I'll explain—sometime," he told her. "Go get some sleep. We'll have to start early because I do have to work."

She nodded and turned. She paused on the stairway, but he had already gone into the kitchen.

She went upstairs and had a cold shower. Due to the heat, it wasn't at all terrible.

She curled up in bed again. His bed. Well, at least a bed in his house.

And she thought that the evening she'd spent with him had been better than anything she had done in a long time. It was easy to be with him. He was everything she might have imagined in a man...

She still knew nothing about him. He could be so cryptic, and so brooding.

The roofers had all been willing to just about bow down to him. Maybe he had paid them well. Maybe people were just extraordinarily helpful because of the storm.

Maybe...

She didn't know anything about him, but she knew him. The scent of him, his smile, the sound of his voice. The way he talked, the way he laughed ...

She rolled over, worried. He was very attractive. He was awakening things within her that had slept peacefully for a long time.

All right, so she was almost dying to touch him ...

And be touched.

After so short an acquaintance.

It was dangerous. She was setting herself up.

Yet ...

What else could she do?

She rolled over and pounded her pillow with that thought. Then she heard his footsteps on the stairs, light, an easy, confident tread.

She thought he paused on the stairway, and her heart began to beat mercilessly.

Was he coming here?

But he did not. She heard his door at the end of the hallway opening and closing.

She closed her eyes again. Sleep, sleep, sleep ...

But sleep did not come easily. It seemed hours that she lay awake. *He owed her. That was what he had said. She shouldn't thank him, because he owed her. What did he mean?*

He'd explain some time ...

She groaned, buried her head in the pillow. And sometime, at long last, she slept.

Andrew was being called a ''dry'' hurricane, meaning that it hadn't dumped too much rain. The storm had moved very quickly, and people were already wondering just what would have happened had it actually sat upon Dade County for any length of time.

It was drizzling in the morning. Katie slept hard and woke to the sound of Drew's voice calling her name.

He was seated by her side on the bed; he had a cup of coffee in his hand, ready to give her.

"You're going to make someone a great wife," she murmured, sliding up to take it.

"Thanks," he said offhandedly. "You've got about ten minutes," he told her, gold eyes glittering as he rose.

"Ten minutes!" She streaked up, the coffee in her hand, and raced toward the bathroom.

"Downstairs, ten minutes!" he said, leaving the room.

She rushed. A sweep across teeth, one through her hair—and a sixty-second makeup job. She found a short-sleeve knit dress among her belongings and shimmied into it, slid into Midge's pumps this time, then quickly checked her camera and equipment. She had discovered a nice cache of film in the garage, so she was set.

Within ten minutes, she was downstairs.

"Ready?" he said, arching a disbelieving brow.

"We're taking the Probe!" Jordan told her delightedly.

"Great," Katie said, "and yes, I'm ready."

"You're very good," he told her.

"Thanks."

The rain had stopped, she was glad to see. But of course, when they were in the car, the radio instantly reminded them that the dousing rain had caused greater disaster for the many homeless people in the area. She thought of how quickly Drew Cunningham had gotten roofers out to maintain what had been left of her home, and she was grateful.

It felt good to be in the car, too. The air-conditioning was on. She hadn't felt really cool in a lifetime, it seemed.

"What a car!" Jordan said.

"Glad you like it."

"Oh, I like everything of yours," Jordan said honestly. Katie turned from the front seat to frown at him. He lifted his hand innocently.

"There!"

They had barely left the sheltered little area of their cul-de-sac when Drew stopped the car. They had come upon an amazing sight—a steel power pole twisted into and out of an Oldsmobile.

"Stop?" he asked Katie.

"Yes, stop, please."

She slipped out of the Probe and quickly started snapping pictures. The power of the wind had been fantastic. She wanted her photos to be important. Photos that would capture that power.

So that it could not be forgotten.

When she finished, Drew drove on in silence. He took her on an amazing odyssey, and at times during their trip, she felt like crying. She couldn't believe what she was seeing. Strip malls with their windows and

contents completely blown out. House after house after house, destroyed. Huge warnings put up in spray
paint—*You loot, we shoot!*

She took pictures of the houses with their warning
signs, their crumpled roofs, their boarded-up windows. The trees that lay in living rooms. They moved
on.

Police were at some of the major intersections, but
traffic moved at a snail's pace. Some drivers were incredibly careful and courteous, and some were incredibly rude. They wound up in a gridlock that took
about fifteen minutes to clear.

He brought her to the hotel where the parking lot
had flooded with seawater, and where the local children were catching fish, barefoot, smiling, despite the
fact that half of them had no homes.

Her camera captured it all.

Finally, she ran out of film.

They moved toward the water, where million-dollar
boats sat in the middle of million-dollar houses. Once
beautiful sleek craft lay atop each other, on shore,
offshore.

They left the water, and Drew told her he was going to have to take her home; he had to go to work.

Katie thanked him, determined that she was going
to drive out again herself, if not this afternoon, then
tomorrow. She might develop this film this afternoon
and see what she had.

Drew returned her and Jordan to the house and left
again. Jordan went upstairs—he wanted to lie down.
Katie went out to the garage and started working with

her film. The task was absorbing. She stayed at it, both pleased and horrified by her pictures. They were definitely some of her best work.

And her best work had come from such tempest . . .

"Mom?" Jordan called to her.

"Yep?"

"It's dark. I've got a flashlight out here, in case you need it."

Katie hung the picture she had been studying and hurried out of the darkroom. Jordan was waiting for her with a flashlight. Of course, she'd had her own with her, but she was still touched by the sight of her son.

And annoyed with herself. Some mother! Her poor child must be starving.

"Want to wait for Drew?" she asked him, "Or are you starving now?"

"He called and said to eat without him, he's going to be very late," Jordan told her. He grinned. "And yes, I'm starving."

"Poor kid!" Katie said, ruffling his hair.

"No," he said, very seriously—too seriously for a ten-year-old boy, "I'm a lucky kid. I've got a roof over my head!"

"Yeah, I guess we are lucky," Katie said. "Come on—let's see what we can scrounge up."

She found a canned ham and sliced and heated it along with canned green beans and canned corn. She was rather impressed with the meal she managed to get together, but though Jordan ate it quickly and hungrily, he stared at his plate with a pained expression when he was done.

"What's wrong?" Katie asked.

"Boy, I sure can't wait to go to Burger King again. Or McDonald's. Wendy's, maybe."

"Thanks!" Katie said.

"I didn't mean anything terrible by that!" Jordan said, and Katie laughed.

"That's all right. I can't wait to go for Thai food again. Or Chinese, or Japanese. Or—"

"A sub sandwich with all kinds of great junk on it!" Jordan finished happily.

"I can't wait for hot water!" Katie told him.

"And I can't wait for air-conditioning."

He helped her clean up. By then, Katie felt hot and sticky, and she went up to take her shower early. She slipped into her white cotton gown and one of her own robes and went downstairs. She sat before the little television, watching the news, which still centered on the storm, then suddenly realized that she needed to try to call Wanda and find out if she had managed all right. The phone was busy. Katie tried again, then again. She decided after a while that Wanda's phone must be out, then, on her last try, she heard Wanda's voice as her friend answered the phone.

"Hello?"

"Wanda?"

"Katie?"

"Yes, it's me. Are you all right?"

"I think so. Katie, I tried to get you! Your phone is out, you know."

"Wanda—my whole house is out. How about you?"

"Well, I'm living in the den," Wanda said. "My bedroom reminds me of Lake Erie. But I'm fine, and I guess I'm going to make it, but oh, is it miserable! Katie, my store doesn't exist anymore! I have no home and no business."

"You were insured, right?"

"Yes, and things will come around, I'm sure, it's just that for the moment... Well, I wake up, then I sweat for a while, and then I cry and sweat for awhile, and then I cry harder because I feel so guilty—I know I could be so much worse off!"

"Wanda, it's a tough time. And it's going to be a tough time."

Wanda lowered her voice. "There's one good thing that has come from it all."

"Oh?"

"The people in my neighborhood association got together to hire an off-duty policeman to watch the area during the evenings. And he's very nice and very good-looking."

Katie grinned. "Well, I'm glad."

"What about you? What are you going to do? Oh, Katie! We can't even meet for lunch—there isn't any place to have lunch."

"Broward County," Katie said.

"If you could only get there!"

Katie thought she heard a car coming into the driveway. "Wanda, take care, and I'll call you again soon, okay?"

"But Katie, where are you? What are you doing?"

"I'm staying with a neighbor, right across the street. I'm in good shape. I'll talk to you soon, promise."

She hung up before Wanda could start asking her questions she definitely didn't want to answer with Drew Cunningham coming home.

She stood and waited for him to come up the walk, looking through the peephole then opening the door when he neared the house. She saw him a moment before he saw her. She was startled by the look of bleak exhaustion in his eyes, and she wanted to reach out to him.

She was living with him—but she wasn't that close to him, she reminded herself.

And then, when he saw her, the look was gone, camouflaged behind his smile.

"You waited up."

"It's the least I can do. I have dinner waiting," she said.

He came in, closed the door and leaned against it. "I could get to like this arrangement," he told her.

She turned quickly, feeling a flush coming to her cheeks, afraid to tell him that she was beginning to like the arrangement herself and that she was beginning to feel far too at home in his house.

"Can I shower first?" he asked her. "I've been working with the roofers down the street, Seth's house. It isn't quite so bad as yours, only one area of the roof was swept away, and they're anxious to get back in. I think they'll be able to do so soon."

Katie paused by the entry to the dining room and kitchen, turning to him.

"Great!" she told him.

She went into the kitchen. He went up the stairs. She set the table attractively for one, then gave them both a wineglass and lit the Sterno to heat the ham and vegetables. When he came down, she set the plate before him.

"Thanks," he said. "You're not joining me."

"I ate with Jordan."

"It's delicious," he told her, taking a bite of the ham.

She smiled. "Thanks. Jordan ate his dinner and told me he couldn't wait to get back to Burger King."

Drew laughed. He poured the wine and sat back, sipping his, watching Katie. She felt herself growing very warm. She sipped her own wine.

"How did your photos come out?"

"Wonderful—horrible," she told him.

He nodded, knowing exactly what she meant. "What are you going to do with them?"

"Send them to some of the papers and magazines," she said. "If I can get to a post office."

"I know the South Miami branch is open. We can drive up tomorrow if you want."

"I can drive myself," she reminded him.

"I don't mind—"

"Right, but if you don't spend half the day playing chauffeur to me, you won't have to stay out all night."

"Some of these guys prefer working at night—it isn't so hot. They're used to working in the sun, but then, they're used to getting into air-conditioning and cold sodas or beers afterward. There's a lot going on at night.''

"And I imagine night will be prime feeding time for mosquitoes pretty soon."

"Mosquitoes—they're already worried about a rat problem, as well," he murmured.

"We are getting an awful lot of trash built up already," she agreed.

It was strange. She felt herself growing warm all over again, just because he was watching her. They had fallen into an incredibly domestic pattern very quickly and very easily. She still didn't know much of anything about him—his life before the storm was a blank—but she felt more and more comfortable with him . . .

More and more intrigued by him, more fascinated. More drawn . . .

"Well!" she said suddenly. "I think I'll go on up to bed. Jordan went to sleep really early—especially for Jordan. He must be trying to catch up. I'll do the same."

She stood. He didn't stop her. He continued to watch her, though, and he smiled slightly, his dark lashes lowering. "No movie tonight? We could see half the classics before this is over."

"No movie tonight," she said softly. She started to turn. His fingers suddenly fell on her hand where she had been holding the back of her chair.

"You're not afraid of being with me suddenly, are you, Katie?"

"Afraid? Of course not."

"Oh."

"Should I be?" she found herself asking.

He shrugged, smiling again. "No, you shouldn't be, but you are. As soon as we get close, you start retreating." His voice grew soft, deep, low...sensual. He stood, meeting her eyes with a certain challenge in the golden depths of his. "And I haven't felt quite so right with anyone in a long, long time."

Katie felt as if her breath had caught somewhere deep in her chest. She couldn't find her voice immediately.

"I barely know you."

"I barely know you. I like what I know."

"I don't know anything about you. I don't know if I'm intruding on anyone else's relationship, I—"

"I'll make it easy. I've been around some. I was married briefly, ten years ago. I was involved in a relationship that split up about a year ago. I've dated since, but no one seriously. Your turn. Tell me about yourself."

"I'm an open book," she said softly.

He arched a brow. "You haven't been serious with anyone since—your husband passed away?"

She shook her head. She wasn't sure if all the blood had drained from her face or if a ton of it had rushed into her cheeks. She felt as if she was burning. And she was afraid. Of herself, of him, of the way the conversation was going.

"I—I really need some sleep," she said, almost desperately.

He nodded, watching her. "Sure. Go on up."

She turned, then turned back. "I forgot to say thank you—"

"You don't need to thank me. I keep telling you that."

"Thanks anyway," she murmured, and left the kitchen.

She took her flashlight and made it up the stairs almost blindly. She hurried into her room, closed the door and leaned against it.

Her heart was hammering. She turned off her flashlight, set it down and stood in the darkness.

In a few minutes, she heard him coming up the stairs.

She didn't know what she was doing; she didn't know at all. But she suddenly opened her door and went into the hallway. The slimmest rays of moonlight seemed to illuminate it. She couldn't see his features, only his silhouette as he stood there before her.

"Katie?" he murmured softly, coming toward her. "Are you all right?"

She could feel his heat, almost as if he touched her with it across the foot of space that separated them. In the pale moonglow she could see the contours and shadows of his handsome features, the way a damp lock of hair hung over his forehead. She could breathe in the subtle scent of him, masculine, clean...alluring.

"Katie?"

"Yes!" she whispered. "I'm—fine."

"Can you see all right?"

"I—don't need to see," she told him. And yet she stood there.

She had been afraid, so she had run away.

Now she was afraid again, so she couldn't come forward.

She didn't need to.

"Katie," he said, very softly.

And she hadn't moved; she was certain she hadn't moved.

Yet suddenly...

She was in his arms. And it seemed that the moon-glow was raining down on them.

And indeed, she could see all that she needed to see.

Chapter 6

Katie wondered vaguely if she needed the darkness, the shadows and the moonlight. Perhaps she could never have done this in daylight or anything other than the pale moonglow that seemed to add a touch of magic and timelessness to the night.

It wasn't that she couldn't see him. She could. When her eyes were open, at least. But she closed her eyes as he kissed her in the hallway, closed her eyes and felt the raw burst of desire with which his lips touched her, the hunger with which he parted them, the passion with which his tongue touched her, swept her mouth. The fever seemed to sweep through her, melting, sweet, touching her lips, radiating down the length of her until she felt liquid.

So this is what it felt like to be touched by him. To know the feel of his hand at her nape, at the small of her back. Caressing her cheek and throat as his lips touched her...

But then his lips broke from hers, and his eyes seemed a pure and glittering gold in the moonlight. His breath escaped with a shuddering sound, but he forced her to look at him in the hallway, to meet the hard, handsome contours of his face and the demand within his eyes.

"Is this what you want?" he whispered tensely.

Was it what she wanted? No, she had wanted the right person to come along, to fall absolutely in love with Jordan, to fall absolutely in love with her, to picnic with her, go to the movies, have dinner, maybe go bowling, come around again and again as the months swept by until she knew it was right...

She hadn't wanted to long for an almost stranger with this sizzle of fire that defied all thought and logic.

"Katie?" He would let her go, she knew. Let her walk away, close the door. And he would close his own. No matter how much desire she felt in the arms that held her, no matter what the tension, the hunger in himself.

"Go to bed, Katie," he said softly. His fingers brushed her cheek.

He turned and started walking away from her. She stood there for the briefest second of indecision, then she ran after him.

He turned just as she went into his arms. She cupped his face, liking the just slightly rough feel of his cheeks between her palms, finding his lips swiftly, hungrily, with her own. She pressed hard against him, loving the strength of his chest, deeply aware of the subtle, arousing, masculine scent of him. She kissed his lips hard, then teased them with a flick of her tongue, delved within them again, searched, played and hungered all the more.

She suddenly found herself off her feet, in his arms, and meeting the hard glitter of his eyes in the moonlight once again. "Katie . . ."

"Last chance," she whispered, keeping her eyes on his. Then she couldn't find the rest of the words she had to say, and merely whispered, "Please."

It was the right word. Swift footsteps and long strides brought them to his door, opened with the nudge of his foot. The moonglow was brighter here, for the boards were down and the French doors that opened to the balcony over the pool area had been thrown open, welcoming the night breeze and the magic of the moonlight.

His room was handsome, striking, masculine. A huge four-poster bed in dark wood faced the open doors. It was covered in a maroon and black patterned comforter, with a pile of satiny black pillows at the headboard. His furniture was deep, rich, hardwood, with a maroon Berber carpet beneath the bed and walls painted in peach that opened the room and saved it from too much darkness.

But the rest of the room blurred. Katie saw the expanse of the bed, the open windows, the moon.

And she saw his face again as he laid her down on the bed, then rose above her.

She wished he'd kiss her again. That he'd come down beside her. That they might shed their clothing while touching, while holding onto the mystery and the sweet impulse. She wished he wouldn't insist on questions...

But he did.

He stood above her, stripping his knit shirt over his head. She stared at his shoulders, his bronze chest, the taut ripple of muscle at his abdomen. The fever took flight within her. He shed his shoes, his socks...

"Katie, I want you to know what you're doing—with whom," he told her.

She felt her cheeks color. "I can go back to your guest room if you like."

He was before her again, his tension bringing a whipcord tightness to his shoulders and chest. He lifted her chin to bring her eyes to his.

"I don't want you to be sorry. You don't know me that well. No regrets on this. No turning back."

"Can't we just have sex?" she tried to say lightly.

But he shook his head. "No regrets. No recriminations," he insisted.

"No regrets," she whispered hoarsely.

He unzipped his jeans, and the sound sent tremors streaking through her.

He stepped from them, easily, naturally, bringing his briefs along with them.

Everything on him was hard and tight and exceptionally aroused. Her eyes immediately fell to the new area of his nakedness, then rose swiftly again, all the color coming back to her cheeks. How strange! She wanted to make love, quickly, desperately, and she still didn't want him to know that she was staring at him. Just days ago they had been strangers, and now he was stark naked just inches away from her.

Not inches away. He swept her into his arms again, stripping the comforter from the bed. She felt his naked flesh against her own, felt each ripple of muscle, each touch against her. Then she found herself lying beneath him, and he was raised above her, legs draped over her.

"One last thing," he told her.

"What?" she asked, swallowing. A part of her wanted to run away in embarrassment.

Another part, a stronger part, knew that she couldn't bear to do so, that it was wonderful to be here, to watch him and try not to watch him, to feel his body against her own.

"Just say, 'Andrew Cunningham, I want you to make love to me. I'll want it in the morning just as badly as I want it now.'"

"Drew, that's not fair," she began, but she broke off as his features tautened and tensed and a small, wry smile curved his lip.

"Why not? I can say it." His hands smoothed her ribs as he spoke, over the terry of her robe, the cotton of her gown. The friction of the material against her flesh seemed exotic. His moving palm came over her breast, the fullness of it, the nipple. The feel of it brought a catch to her throat. Her lips went dry, her breath came too quickly. And the sound of his voice added richly to every sweet touch of fire that stroked its way through her. "I wanted you from the moment I first touched you. From the very second I picked you up—"

"Out of the mud?" she asked breathlessly.

"Hey, some people like mud," he teased softly. But then the smile faded, and all she saw was the golden glow in his eyes as he continued. "I wanted you then, when your clothing was against you like a second skin. I wanted you later, when you were freshly showered, dressed in my robe, and I wanted you later, when you were fully dressed. I want you now, and I know that come morning, I'll never try to delude myself that the storm, the darkness, the moon in the night had anything to do with it."

His hand moved while he spoke. Slow, erotic, above the fabric still, yet using the fabric to make every motion more sensual.

"Long-winded, aren't you?" she asked him.

"I want the words, Katie."

She slipped her arms around him, holding tight, burying her face against his chest. "I want you, Andrew Cunningham. And I won't regret anything in the morning. I—"

That was it. It seemed he had talked for so long. Suddenly, he wasn't talking anymore, and he didn't seem to need any more words from her. His lips fell upon hers with a passion that was staggering, sweeping away her breath, her thoughts. His fingers were on the tie of her robe, undoing it swiftly and deftly. His lips left hers for her throat, and he started on the tiny buttons of her nightgown, his fingers amazingly dexterous. The gown slipped from her shoulders. His lips touched her flesh where it was bare. Her fingers dug into his shoulders. His fingers swept beneath the hem of the gown, and the rough, erotic feel of his palm swept up her thigh, fingers stroking the soft inner flesh, curling into the elastic of her bikini panties.

But he didn't strip them away. His lips left her flesh, and he was sitting, reaching for her. "I really wanted you when I was finding all your silky things thrown around your room," he murmured. "I wanted to see them on you . . ."

He slipped the robe from her shoulders. He tried to pull the cotton gown from her body, but her weight was on it. "You could help," he whispered.

"What? Oh!" But it didn't matter, because he swept her up, dragged the gown away, and this time, when he came down upon her, she felt the smooth heat of his flesh against her own, and the sheer pleasure and intimacy of it nearly made her weep aloud.

His fingers threaded through hers. His lips touched down on hers, on her throat, on her lips once again.

His tongue found the peak of her breast. Her breath caught. A gasp escaped her. He played with the hardening tip of her nipple, laving, touching, wetting, teasing, taking it fully into his mouth.

His head moved lower against her body, his tongue slipping into her navel, trailing to her hip. Her fingers tore into his hair. She discovered her body writhing against his in a sweet, natural rhythm of its own. She'd forgotten so much, and yet . . .

Maybe she'd never quite known this sweet hunger, wanting something, needing . . . someone.

She tugged at his hair, trying to draw his face to hers, longing to touch him, longing to feel the burning that now blazed between her thighs. "Drew." She whispered his name, then again, and still he didn't seem to feel her tug on his hair, for he still touched and stroked her body, bringing her so close to a pinnacle, drawing back just slightly. The molten heat of his kiss was low over her abdomen. His fingertips stroked her upper thighs, higher, higher, then came brushing through the soft down at their juncture.

"Drew . . ."

He rose above her, his hair rakishly disheveled, his features tense, his lip curling into the slightest smile. "If you've waited this long, Mrs. Wells, it needs to be good. Damned good," he whispered softly, a note of tenderness in the passion of his voice.

He rolled her to her stomach, and she felt the searing liquid heat of his kiss at her nape, moving down her spine. Down, down, his fingertips touching, caressing. She could bear it no longer and turned in his arms, kissing his lips, feverishly touching his shoulders and chest with her fingertips, planting liquid kisses where she had touched, fascinated by his warmth, his vibrance, the ripple and life of his every movement. She laid her palm on his chest and allowed it to flow slowly down the length of him until she closed her fingers around the length of his aroused sex, drawing a fantastic groan from him, one that seemed to tear from his chest, to sweep them both away.

And she was swept away, for she was suddenly beneath him again, and the sweet, taunting play was over, the wild ride to ecstasy had begun. She trembled uncontrollably as his body seemed to sink into the very depths of her. She could feel the impalement to her heart, and with it came the slow spread of a radiating heat throughout her, as if the ball of the sun had burst within her, and golden laps of flame flared their way into her body and limbs. She met his eyes, and in the golden moonlight they seemed like gold, glowing suns, penetrating, demanding all that she could give, and giving that spectacular warmth in return. She couldn't quite meet that golden gaze, and she let her lashes flutter over her eyes while she clung to him and let the hunger and natural rhythms take them away, soaring, stretching...

She had all but reached the most fantastic pinnacle when he suddenly pulled from her. The subtropic breeze whispered in from the French doors, covering her flesh softly, sensually. She felt his stroke again, his kiss, and a frenzy filled her unlike anything she had known before. He touched her again and again, the liquid of his kiss against her cooling flesh. She tore at his hair, whispering desperately for him. Yet he took his leisure, kissing, caressing, demanding every intimacy. When she was all but in tears she felt him rise above her again, and the moonlight rippled on his bronze, tense shoulders, and in his eyes she saw that he had carefully built her hunger to match his own, and that his own desire was now erotically explosive...

His hands cradled her buttocks and he held her while he thrust rapid fire into her again and again and again until...

Climax swept her. So hard and so strong that for endless seconds she seemed to drift in a darkness where stars burst against a black sky. Then she was aware again, aware of the night, of the breeze, of the man, of the rock-hard tension in his features and the fierce constriction of his body as he thrust within her one last time, groaned and shuddered, his body slick and hard atop her own.

He fell quickly to her side, but brought her with him, his arms around her.

She had been so hot, on fire. Now the breeze whispered over her and she shivered, the air felt so cool. He pulled a sheet over them. He rose above her on an elbow, seeking her eyes.

"You all right?" he asked her softly.

She met his gaze, feeling her lips curl into a smile. "Fine," she told him.

"I just wanted—"

"It was."

"Umm," he said. "Made you wonder what you'd been missing all these years?"

Her smile deepened, but she shook her head. "I haven't missed anything," she assured him. "Because I never felt that it was...*right,* before. Not since...I was married."

He stroked her cheek and very tenderly kissed her lips. "You're a very wise young lady, Mrs. Wells."

"Not so young."

"Hardly ancient. Nearly...perfect."

"Nearly?"

"All right, perfect. But it's frightening to think of you letting such things go to your head."

He cradled her against him, her back to his front, his lips close to her ear, his hand resting just beneath her breast. Katie felt the breeze again, moving over her shoulders, but she wasn't shivering anymore, not with the heat of his body around her.

Dear God, but she felt wonderful. Her house was demolished, she hadn't felt hot water in ages, and she spent her days sweltering.

And yet she felt she had come upon just a touch of heaven.

She felt his hand moving again, rubbing her belly. Heard his husky, tantalizing whisper at her ear. "Um, I'm so tempted. But, ah, well, you're new at this again, I wouldn't want to push things too far...wear you out."

The last was suggestive. As suggestive was the intimate feel of his hand slipping down her body.

She turned in his arms, trembling as her movement brought his touch very intimately against her. She could feel his arousal, and that seemed to bring a sweet dizziness to her.

"I don't think I'll wear out," she murmured thoughtfully. "Actually, I think I'd be fine. Unless, of course, you might be about to wear out?'' she asked innocently.

''I don't think you can wear me out tonight, Mrs. Wells,'' he said, his voice husky, his eyes absolutely devilish. ''You're more than welcome to try.''

She found herself smiling. Until his lips touched hers. Until the fever mounted.

It had been so long...

But she didn't regret the time at all, and she was glad that things could be so right tonight.

She did wear out first, dozing even as she heard his soft chuckle, and felt him stretch out beside her, their flesh still touching. This was delicious, as well, sleeping this way, feeling his arms, feeling the closeness...

She must have slept like a log. She seemed in a fog as she struggled to awaken, and she did so because she was being called and heard a distant tapping, as well...

''Mom?''

She bolted up in a wild panic, wide awake in a flash. She couldn't believe that, no matter how wonderful the night had been, she had forgotten that she was a mother, with a ten-year-old son in the same house. A son who would naturally rise and look for her.

''Jordan!'' she whispered.

But Drew was already up, pulling on a bathrobe. ''I'll take him down with me and tell him to give you a few more minutes to sleep,'' he assured her calmly.

''Oh, God!'' she whispered miserably. ''How could I have forgotten about Jordan, I—''

"Katie—" His voice was softer than hers when he leaned over her. "Katie, nothing is wrong. He won't mind coming downstairs with me. And besides, you don't even need to go out in the hallway."

"What?"

He strode quickly across the room, pulling what had looked like an ornamental leaf on one of the built-in shelves against the wall. The shelf came forward as he pulled it, and she saw that it led to a shelf in her room.

She arched a brow.

"Don't you give me that look," he warned her. "It's only here in case the room should ever be used as a nursery."

"Mom?"

Katie leaped up and darted to the opening, then paused and streaked back for her nightgown and robe. The hidden door closed behind her. Even as she called out to Jordan—trying to sound suitably sleepy—she heard Drew exiting his room and coming into the hallway to meet Jordan.

"Morning, Jordan," she heard Drew say. "Katie, we'll go on down and start the coffee on the Sterno," he called loudly. "Take your time getting ready."

"I'll—I'll be right down!" she called.

But she wasn't right down. She leaped into the shower and felt the daylight flood of emotions sweep through her. What had she been doing? She wasn't alone, she had a son. She was living with this man, she shouldn't be sleeping with him, as well.

No, she should be sleeping with people she wasn't living with? she taunted herself.

She dressed, trying to tell herself that it was really fine. She needed a life that went beyond her photography and her son's sports and parent-teacher night. And she shouldn't be berating herself. Drew had known that she would, which was why he had made her talk, made her see that she really did want to do what she had done ...

So what was she afraid of?

Afraid that she had suddenly found something good, so good that she would hate to lose it?

She dressed and brushed her hair. Neither love nor life came with any guarantees. She couldn't stop living because of that. She had to take a few chances ...

She had taken a chance.

And... It had been worth it, she assured herself. No matter what came in the future, she would be glad for last night.

At last, she went downstairs to the kitchen. Jordan was at the sink, carefully washing a few dishes.

She wondered if the word guilt was written all over her face.

Jordan smiled at her. "You're slow, Mom. Drew already made coffee and oatmeal, showered and went out."

"Wow, I am slow," Katie said, pouring herself a cup of coffee. "Where did Drew go? To work?"

Jordan shook his head. "Not yet. Some people came to the door, and he went out with them. He said he'd be back in a little while and that you shouldn't worry. There are some envelopes and packing materials upstairs in his drafting room if you want to mail some of your photographs. He's got express labels and everything, he said. Do you know where you're sending your stuff, Mom?''

"Yep, for now. You know what I think I'm going to do this time?'' she asked him.

"A book?'' Jordan suggested.

"How'd you guess?''

Jordan shrugged. "There should be a book on this. Photos that show what happened.''

She ruffled his hair. "You're right. There should be a book—and I'm certain there will be lots of books. And mine is going to be one of them. But for the moment, I'm going to get my pictures and pack them up for mailing. I'll be back in a little bit.''

Her little bit was longer than she had intended, but she had to go to the garage for her photographs—all of them eight by tens in black and white. Then she had to fill out various mailing slips and dig through Drew's drawing room long enough to find the backing she needed for the mailers. When she came downstairs, she found Jordan alone in the kitchen, reading a book. *Old Yeller.* She smiled and poured herself a second cup of coffee. She sipped it, watching Jordan. After a moment, he looked up at her. "It's really very good,'' he said defensively.

"*Old Yeller* is a great book. Sad, but great.''

He shrugged. "There's not much else to do.''

"Reading is good for you.''

"It's not like I *never* read.''

"And it's not like you read all the time.'' She glanced at her watch. They were well into the afternoon now. She sipped her coffee, then told Jordan, "I think I'm going to see what's going on. Drew seems to have some kind of pull with repair people. Well, of course, I guess he should. He's a builder himself. He probably contracts these same people for his jobs."

"I'll tag along," Jordan told her.

"I thought that the book was good."

"It is—but the dog just died."

Katie hid her smile. Jordan was too old to cry in front of her over a book.

And no one was too old to feel like crying when that poor old yellow dog died!

"Come on, kid," she told him, setting an arm around his shoulder.

Drew stood with Giles in the hallway of Katie's house, looking at the beams that remained in her roof. "I swear to you, Drew," Giles was telling him, "I checked the records all backwards and forwards. I did your house—you know, of course, because you were around for the construction. But I wasn't given this job. The last three here were completed last November. And in November, I was sent up to the development in Palm Beach. I don't know what the hell happened here, I can't even find a work order on the place."

"Who inspected it?" Drew demanded.

Giles riffled through the papers on his clipboard. "Let me see . . . A. Alonso."

Drew let loose an expletive. "That bastard has been taking bribes left and right for years."

Giles shook his head. "But the staples were legal. I imagine they might be outlawed now—"

"They've been ignoring the building codes for years, dammit, putting up shoddy construction. My dad used to complain about it. Inspectors were taking bribes when he was still alive."

"Drew, I'm sure that inspectors were taking bribes way back when the pyramids were being done."

Despite his anger and aggravation, Drew had to smile. He liked Giles a lot, and he depended on him. Giles was a man who took tremendous pride in quality workmanship.

"The point is, everyone knows that *Hunnicunn* doesn't put up a roof like this! And there were three of them—in my own damned development!"

"Well, I checked all that I could, Drew. And it seems that all the work orders were signed by your own hand."

Drew shook his head. "You know that I would never have okayed something like this."

Giles shrugged uncomfortably. "Then it would seem that someone high up in your corporation is skimming from somewhere. It's a horrible thing to say, but . . ." His voice trailed away.

Drew gritted his teeth and forced himself to admit the truth.

Someone was skimming. And Drew had grown careless; he hadn't read everything that came before him—he had just gotten accustomed to being busy and signing his name when paperwork was put before him.

He lowered his head, closing his eyes for a minute, remembering his father. His dad had been gone a long time now, but Drew could still remember the pride with which he'd always said that his boy would grow up and build good houses, quality houses. The kind that would last, that would protect people in a storm.

It didn't help his sick feeling any when he read in the newspapers that over eighty thousand homes had been lost.

His shouldn't have been among them. He had built the houses in his development to withstand those winds. His own house had withstood them, and so had the Holloways', the Hamptons' and the Thomasons'.

The three that had sustained the devastating damage had all had the same flaw.

Cheap roofing. And he knew that stapled roofs had not been in his plans for the homes.

Most of his main office had been untouched, but a number of records were missing. Jeannie, his secretary, who had made it in to work yesterday, seemed at a loss to explain it.

Not that it mattered. He had never okayed such practices, but the homes were his responsibility—his fault. But he'd be damned if something like this was ever going to happen to him again. He had to have the truth.

He set his hands on his hips, staring at the roof. If it hadn't been for the storm, he might never have known how three of the houses in the development had been built. But because of Andrew, he was standing in Katie Wells's house, looking at the destruction around him. She had salvaged a lot, but pieces of her life were still here, ruined. A sodden photo book, caught beneath the corner of a crushed sofa. A single baby shoe, blown into the living room from somewhere. Jordan's, he imagined. Something Katie had meant to keep forever, like a flower pressed into the pages of a book.

This was all his fault . . .

But he'd slept with her last night anyway.

He gritted his teeth. Well, he thought angrily, he had never lied to her. He'd told her he was an architect and a builder; he had even said he had been there every day when his house was being built.

He hadn't lied . . . but he hadn't told her the truth. He hadn't made her see the truth. She kept thanking him. Damn, if only she'd quit thanking him. He should have told her.

Maybe not. If he had told her, he might never have had last night. And he didn't think he could trade last night for anything—not even honesty. Somewhere, during the years, he had become so damned jaded. Then he'd plucked Katie out of the wind and the rain and . . .

She had been everything he had been missing. Arousing, at first, with the gown clinging to her breasts and nipples with an amazing appeal. He hadn't lied about that—he had wanted her from the moment he had first seen her, touched her.

He hadn't known how much he wanted her until he came to realize that he loved the sound of her voice, the sweet, low, slightly husky alto. He loved her eyes.

Blue as a clear morning sky. He loved the way she could pitch in so quickly, the way she could make the best of a situation. The way she could rush in wildly— then listen with gravity and wisdom.

He'd loved coming home...

To dinner, to Katie. To Jordan. In all his life, he'd never had a situation quite like this.

His dad had died, killed in a building accident the summer Drew had turned eighteen. He hadn't wanted to go to college then. But his mother had reminded him that Harvard had been his father's dream, and so he had gone. His first few years out of school he had worked like a maniac for other people. Maybe that was why he had lost Janet.

Maybe they had just grown apart, or maybe they had never been meant for each other. It didn't matter. She had wanted a sports car, he'd wanted children. They could have had both in time, he was certain. But Janet hadn't wanted to wait to have what she wanted, and he didn't know whether she had ever cheated on him. All he knew was that he had come in at midnight one time too many and found her gone.

He'd filed the papers. She'd wanted to fix things then. It had been too late.

Maybe he should have had more patience.

Maybe not. He'd heard she was on her fourth husband.

But his marriage hadn't soured him. It had put things in perspective. He had formed his own company with one of his father's old friends, a man named Henry Hunnington, thus Hunnicunn, a combination of names. Drew had given Hunnington the first half of the name since he had supplied a great deal of the money.

After a few years, though, he'd made back Mr. Hunnington's money, and much more. He'd had a wild streak then, dating often—and with variety. Then time—and exhaustion—had toned him down. He'd settled into relationship with a catalogue model named Amanda Trent, and he'd never quite figured out what went wrong, he only knew that it had gone wrong for him. He hadn't had too much to say to her, and he found himself wanting to watch the football game rather than listen to her.

He started going out of town. Often.

Maybe that was why he'd been gone when his crew had been doing the roof on Katie's house.

Well, he couldn't go back. He couldn't undo it. He couldn't give people back anything that they had lost.

He could only promise to see to it that he would build better in the future.

And find out what the hell was going on in his own office.

"Keep me posted if you find out anything," Drew told Giles.

Giles nodded gravely. "When we can, I imagine that you want all these roofs completely redone."

"Exactly," Drew said. "I'm taking a walk on over to the Hamptons to meet Ted. He's moving back into his own place and needs a little help boarding up some broken windows. Call me if you need me. I'll be heading back to my house after that—I'm going to drive Katie to the post office.''

Alone, he determined. Not that he didn't like Jordan. He did. He liked the boy very much. But he had to talk to Katie. He had to explain to her—late as it might be—that he wasn't just a builder.

He was her builder.

He should have gotten out the words, plain and blunt, before. He could have answered her so easily, so many times.

Katie, don't thank me! I'm the reason you don't have a home of your own, I'm the one responsible for your roof.

But the words hadn't come. Maybe he hadn't been able to say them because he hadn't been able to believe what had happened.

He had to explain it all to her. Today.

''Remember, let me know anything at all that you can find out,'' he told Giles grimly.

Giles nodded and gave him a wave as Drew left Katie's house and headed across the street.

He didn't see Katie. He missed her because he slipped into the Hamptons' house just as she was coming out of his.

If he'd only thought to stop and talk to her then . . .

But he couldn't know what the day was destined to bring.

Chapter 7

Katie and Jordan looked up and down the street but didn't see Drew.

"Wonder where he got to?" Katie said to Jordan.

"Don't know," Jordan said. "But look—the roofers are back at our house again."

"Let's go say hi and find out what they're up to," Katie suggested.

They walked across the jungle of plant life and debris that had once been the beautifully landscaped circle for the cul-de-sac and came to their house. Katie paused at the door. "Hello!" she called.

Giles came into her living room. She realized she was listening for a squishing sound. Then she saw that all the carpeting had been pulled up. The floor was tile and didn't look bad at all.

"Hi, there," Giles said. "Just taking a few structural notes. Need anything? Can I help you?"

Katie smiled. "Not unless you've got a magic wand that can put everything back together," she told him lightly.

"Sorry, fresh out!" he told her.

"Do you know where Drew is?" she asked him.

"Across the street, at the Hampton house."

"Thanks," she said.

As she and Jordan crossed the road, she saw a sleek new Mazda pulling into her driveway. She hesitated, shading her eyes from the sun, watching as an older man, at least in his sixties and perhaps in his seventies, stepped from the car. He was spry and straight, whatever his age, and he stared at her house for a long moment. Then Giles came from the house, hailing the old man, and the old man called out to him in turn.

Someone they worked with, Katie decided.

"Who's that?" Jordan asked.

She shrugged. "I don't know."

"There are strangers all over our house!" Jordan commented.

"Well, there are strangers all over what's left of our house," she agreed. "He must be with the roofers—Giles seems to know him."

Jordan shrugged and walked beside her. "We're going to the Hamptons?" he said.

She stopped. What was she doing? Following Drew all over the neighborhood?

But as she paused, Sophie Hampton opened her front door and called out cheerfully, "Katie! Come in.

Of course, it's awfully hot inside, but it's awfully hot outside, too. Len made it up to the grocery store in South Gables this afternoon so guess what—we've got real live *ice* tea! Come have some.''

"Ice!" Jordan said appreciatively.

Katie grinned and started up the walk. "Thanks, Sophie. Ice tea sounds fabulous.''

Sophie smiled and led them inside. She had a nice, comfortable home with handmade afghans over her sofas and embroidered cushions set invitingly about. Katie and Jordan followed her through the living room to the kitchen, which looked over what was left of the patio.

"Have a seat, please.''

"Thanks, Sophie.''

Sophie was busy digging into the ice chest in front of her refrigerator. "I hear you've been getting some fabulous photos," Sophie told her.

"Sad photos,'' she told Sophie.

"Yes, but then, that's part of life, Katie, you know that.''

Katie nodded, accepting a miraculously cold and frosty glass from Sophie. She sipped the tea. Delicious. She set the glass against her face.

"Wow! You can wear it and drink it!" Jordan said, doing the same.

Sophie laughed, putting her own glass against her forehead. "You're right. Two luxuries in one!''

"I need a photo of this," Katie murmured.

Sophie grinned, then grew serious. "Drew says your photos are excellent. You're sending them out, right?''

Katie nodded. "I'm going to go mail some soon. In fact, I was wondering if Drew was still around. If he's busy, I'm going to take a drive out myself."

"He's over at Ted's now. They're just patching up the last of the broken windows. They've swept out all the glass, Drew and that nice young man, Giles."

Katie nodded, keeping a straight face. Only a lady Sophie's age could possibly refer to Giles as a nice *young* man.

"Giles and that cute little thing—that assistant of his, I think his name is Sean—have done a good job patching up the roof for the time being. Ted is missing a few carpets and windows, but otherwise his place is starting to look good again."

"That's wonderful," Katie said.

"Yours was the worst, I understand," Sophie said, shaking her head.

"But we're all right. And that's what matters. I've realized that more and more in the past few days," Katie told her. "I'm not in the streets or trying to live in a tent or anything." She felt a flush coming to her cheeks, and she swallowed her tea in a rush. No, she wasn't living on the streets, or in a tent. She was...

Sleeping with Andrew Cunningham. She had to stop thinking about it, she told herself, feeling like an idiot. Sophie couldn't possibly look at her and know such a thing!

She stood up. "I'm going to drive up to the South Miami post office. If you see Drew, will you tell him where I've gone?"

"Of course, dear. Oh, and Len and I have a case of lobster tails that we've got to barbecue tonight. We're trying to have the entire neighborhood over. It will be much better if we all eat the lobster—it will be deadly in the trash!"

Katie smiled. Sophie had told her once about Len's lobster tails. He cracked them open and cooked them with a pat of butter on each over charcoals.

It was probably a meal just deadly with cholesterol, but it sounded absolutely wonderful.

"We'll be back," Katie promised.

Jordan asked if he could stay behind, and Sophie said she'd be delighted to watch him. Katie thanked her and left him, then headed to Andrew Cunningham's house for her mail. She worried a bit about not being able to lock the door every time she came and went, but he was in the neighborhood and didn't think anything could happen.

The twenty-minute ride up the highway stretched into an hour and a half. The traffic was terrible, bumper to bumper. Every light on the highway remained out. Each time a traffic volunteer raised a hand for her mass of cars to stop, she glanced at the gas tank, which was running low. She saw a gas station that was open—with a mile-long line of cars waiting. It didn't matter. She had to get gas.

The line was awful. Cars were stuck trying to come and go around the tanks. People were jumping out of their cars, swearing at each other.

A huge, fat man and a tiny woman got into a shouting match. Katie bit her lip, watching them.

Then she remembered she had her camera. She stepped from her car and started taking pictures.

For a moment, she thought the fat man and the tiny woman were going to come over and deck her.

But then they both started laughing and apologized to each other, and suddenly they were telling each other how they had survived the storm.

Finally, Katie got to the pumps. She filled her tank and paid.

An hour after she had pulled off the highway, she was back on it. Tense, tired, hot and sticky, she was in the bumper-to-bumper traffic. And twenty minutes after that, she reached the post office.

There was another hour-long line.

Generators kept fans going, but the heat was unbearable. Finally, though, her photos were mailed. She was in her car, blasting the air-conditioning into her face. But after a moment, she turned it off.

She didn't think she could stand another hour-long wait at a gas station with some people being marvelously patient while others cursed and shouted.

Even if she did get great pictures.

By the time she made it to the cul-de-sac and Drew's house, she was ready to tear out her hair. She walked in and called, "Hello?" No one answered, and she hurried up the stairs, bursting into the guest room and falling flat on the bed.

She felt horrible. She was sticky from the heat. She rose mechanically and went into the bathroom.

She started the spray in the shower stall, then stripped and stepped in. She sat down, letting the wa-

ter fall over her face and hair and body. The traffic
had left her close to tears. No matter how hard she
tried to tell herself she had been lucky, the misery of
getting a few miles down a ravaged highway suddenly
seemed like too much. Her nerves were stripped and
raw.

"Katie!"

She heard her name called. She couldn't quite
manage to move.

Even when she heard herself being called more ur-
gently, she couldn't get up the energy to stand or even
cry out.

"Katie!"

She jumped then—her name had been roared. The
bathroom door burst open, then the shower door was
pulled open.

"Katie, what in God's name is the matter with you?
Why didn't you answer me?" Drew demanded angrily.

"Why didn't you knock?" she demanded furiously
in return. She could shout or cry, it was one or the
other. "It may be your house but you have no damned
right—"

"You scared the hell out of me! I saw you come in
and you wouldn't answer!"

"I don't have to answer if I'm in the shower!"

"You have to answer because the door was un-
locked and because there's more problems with looters now than ever after the storm."

"But your house isn't ripped up—"

"Is a thief going to care?"

"I'm fine!" she raged to him. "Since I don't have a key, I've been leaving the door open—"

"But you're inside the house now!"

"How am I to know for sure that you've left with a key?" she demanded, her voice rising with every word.

"If you had just answered me," he roared.

Something inside her snapped. Her fingers had been curling into the washcloth that lay at her side, and she suddenly lifted it and flung it at him.

It was hardly a deadly missile. But it was sodden and cold, and it hit him right in the face.

For all his wonderful features, the man did have a hell of a temper. As the cloth landed on his head, soaking his face and hair, causing water to drip over his shoulders and chest, she found the energy to leap up at last, backing against the shower wall, waiting for another explosion.

But none came. He pulled the cloth from his face, stared at it, stared at her. Then he said lightly. "Hmm, that felt good." Then before Katie knew it, he was stripping off his wet shirt, slipping from his shoes, unzipping his jeans and joining her.

He stood under the stream of water and gazed at her. There wasn't an inch of distance between their wet bodies. Her eyes were wide on his; she stood still in absolute astonishment.

"Bad day, huh?" he asked.

"Horrible!" she whispered. Then she burst into tears.

It was absurd. She hadn't cried when her house had been coming down on top of her, and she hadn't cried when she had thought the banyan tree and the storm were going to unite to kill her. She hadn't cried when she had seen the damage to her home or when she had tried to tell herself just how very lucky she had been.

And now, ridiculously, she was in tears. She was worn out. The traffic had done what the storm hadn't.

"Katie, Katie!"

She was suddenly in his arms. He was smoothing her wet hair, kissing her forehead, brushing her lips. "It's all right."

"It's not all right, I shouldn't be doing this!" she choked out between sobs.

"Everyone is doing it, why not you?" he asked. "And it's all right, it's all right. It's really going to be all right."

She found herself in his arms as he lifted her up. He slammed the faucet to turn off the water and carried her out of the shower.

"We're soaking your house," she told him.

He shrugged.

"Drew, I'm all wet."

"I'll dry you."

But he carried her straight to the bed, lying down with her. He stayed at her side, stroking her hair, whispering that it was going to be all right. She believed him. She started to apologize.

"I don't know what—what got into me. I don't act like that. I—"

"Katie, my secretary, Jeannie, is the most capable human being I've ever met. Some little thing upset her the other day, and she was in torrents. People here have been through a trauma. There will be many crying jags before it's all over. We're human.''

She smiled suddenly. ''And have you burst into tears?''

''Well, not yet. Not over this, but...''

''Men don't cry.''

''They sure do. I shed buckets when my dad died.''

She turned to look at him more closely. She was suddenly very afraid. She was falling in love with him.

''Feel better?'' he asked her softly.

''Ah...yes.''

''I can make you feel even better,'' he promised. His voice was low and husky. Sensual, insinuative. And still...

She was amazed at what it seemed to do to her. Fire leaped into her. Longing swept her every limb.

Perhaps it wasn't amazing. They were both naked on a bed, slick, clean, wet...

''No,'' she told him. ''I'm going to make you feel better,'' she promised softly.

He started to speak, but she rose to her knees, pushing him back when he started to rise on his elbows. She brought her lips to his, kissing him softly. He tried to capture her nape, hold her to the kiss, but she moved too swiftly. She dusted her fingers over his chest, following her touch with the brush of her lips and tongue. Now she moved slowly, very slowly, sensually stroking his body with hers as she moved against him. She felt the sweet fire fill her with a greater force as his flesh seemed to burn beneath her, as his muscles constricted and rippled at her slightest caress. Her hands stroked over his hips, closed over his sex. A low groan escaped him, and she buried her face against the flat plane of his belly. A shudder gripped him and she found herself encased in his arms again, lifted high, brought atop him. He slowly brought her down, meeting her eyes with golden fire in his as her body sank to be impaled by his. Tiny convulsions gripped her as he seemed to fill her. She cried out, leaning against him, her neck gripped and his lips passionately locked with hers as his hips began to rock, as his hands slid over her buttocks, molding them together.

Moments later, she felt the earth shake, the sky explode, then she felt his arms tenderly around her as she seemed to float to some place on earth. Her eyes were closed, and she felt completely sated, almost like a very well fed cat. The tensions had eased from her; the breeze coming in felt gentle and caressing. She realized she was exhausted.

"I guess we should get up," she murmured, easing against him. "Sophie is planning her party. Jordan—"

"Jordan is helping Len crack the tails—I was just over there. He isn't coming back to the house for awhile," Drew assured her.

Jordan was fine. No one was waiting for her. She relaxed completely.

Drew was still for a few minutes. He was lying on his back, staring at the ceiling, his head on the pillow.

"Katie, I need to talk to you about the storm," he began.

She groaned. "No."

"Katie—"

"Please," she whispered. "Not now, please, just let me forget it for a few minutes."

He was silent. She curled closer to him. She didn't want to think about the rest of the world. Not for awhile. This was too wonderful—making love with someone she was wildly attracted to, someone she cared about...

Someone she was falling in love with.

She didn't want to think about the danger of it. Not now. She wanted to lie in comfort beside him, feeling cared for, feeling cherished. Very relaxed, sweetly sleepy.

He didn't speak. She felt his gentle touch on her back just before she fell asleep.

Drew lay beside her for awhile, lower lip caught between his teeth. He wanted to keep touching her.

He didn't want to wake her. Today, Katie was aware of what their lives had become. She was tough, he knew. But it was hard for anyone to see the shattered community and accept what it would take to put it back together.

After a moment, he rose. He drew the comforter over her since the breeze might be cool on her damp, naked flesh. He paused a moment, appreciating the woman he was coming to...

Want.

Need.

Love?

She was so tempting, with her smooth, silky flesh, her dusky rose nipples a splash of alluring color against the rise of her breasts. She was curled in a sensual curve on her side, derriere rounded and perfect, waist slim, limbs long and shapely.

He dropped the comforter, reminding himself that she was sleeping.

He sighed, walking through the open French doors to the balcony. He'd wanted to talk to her so badly. He needed to explain what had happened—or at least explain that he didn't quite know himself.

He closed his eyes, thinking about Hunnicunn. His partner had died. Hunnington's daughter owned shares, and she made her presence known in the office now and then. If she had asked for his signature, he might have put it on something without giving it attention.

But he always read what he signed, or at least skimmed it.

Who else, who else?

He had employed people he trusted, people he thought shared his visions of what homes should be. Giles was an important member of the team. So was Andrea Hunnington—when she was in the mood, not flying around the Riviera. She was chairman of the board and president of the corporation; Andrew was vice president. Two of the men who had worked with his father, Harry Easton and Sam Jaffe, had come all the way with him. They still worked on the sites often, just as he did. But they were also officers, assistant vice presidents. His mother was on the board, but she stayed out of the office, giving her opinion only during an occasional meeting. Then there was his sister, Reva, who had refused a title from him but liked to come in and work on designs with him.

That was it, really. No one else could possibly have changed the designs or the plans or the order forms.

His mother hadn't done it. Nor his sister.

Andrea? Why? She had more money than Midas.

And he couldn't imagine who among them would have changed the houses.

But someone had.

And if it hadn't been for the storm...

But the storm had come. And the corporation was, for all practical purposes, his. The responsibility was his.

But someone had skimmed off a great deal of money. Who?

A bitterness swept him. Who, indeed? He wished he knew.

He wished he could tell Katie. He couldn't, but he still had to explain to her just exactly who he was. Maybe she would understand.

And maybe she wouldn't.

He swore softly and got dressed, determined to leave her sleeping in peace. He had just slipped into his shoes when he heard a knocking at the front door. He hurried down to answer it. He'd let her sleep awhile, then come back to take her to the party that would begin shortly next door.

Katie woke slowly, feeling greatly refreshed. She had to pause for a moment and remember why she was here, but then she smiled. "Drew?" she called. He didn't answer. She rose, peeked out the door and called his name again. Still no answer.

She decided on another shower. After a few minutes, she grew chilled, so she scrubbed herself and jumped out, shivering as she toweled dry. She dressed in denim shorts and a cool cotton top. Night was coming; the sun was down, but the heat still clung everywhere.

Andrew and Jordan hadn't returned, and she figured maybe they were at Sophie's, hungry for the lobster tails. Katie decided to go over.

Amazingly, there was something like a party going on. A radio was playing—music instead of news. The front door was locked, so Katie walked around the back.

The fallen screen from the Hampton's pool had been completely cleared away, and the patio had been swept and cleared of all debris. The pool still looked like a mud pit, but around it, Sophie had made everything neat and clean. Len was at the barbecue, which had been set very low so that he could sit on a folding chair and watch his lobster tails. He was deep in conversation with Ted Barlow. Jordan was playing some kind of card game with Amy Keogh and another little girl who had to be the Thomasons' child. Jordan was by far the oldest in the group, but he seemed happy enough to play with the girls, and Katie decided that at this point, anyone under the age of twenty had to look like fun to him.

"Katie!"

She turned quickly from the children to see that Midge was calling her. She waved and joined the young blond woman.

"Isn't this wonderful?" Midge said, leading the way into the kitchen. "I'm so sick to death of all the canned stuff we have. Lobster tails! In the middle of all this."

"Not only that, but the most delicious lobster tails you'll ever have, I promise," Sophie said, joining them at the open French doors that led from the patio. "And we've got barbecued potatoes, as well, a nice green salad—all right, so it's just a wee bit wilted—and Midge has made some kind of a no-bake chocolate dessert, so we're really feasting."

"It sounds wonderful," Katie said. "What can I do?"

"Have a seat," Sophie told her. "We're just waiting for Seth and Drew to come back from the Keoghs—they've been fixing up over there today—and then we'll start. Come in, have a seat at the table."

Katie followed her, smiling when she saw Susan Keogh sitting at the table. The woman was very pretty, now that she was dressed and calm and not dripping as Katie had seen her in the very early hours of the storm. She had huge dark eyes and light hair and a quick smile. She stood up as Katie came near, giving her a warm hug. "Katie! It's so wonderful to see you—I've been meaning to see how you were before now, but you know how things are going. Thank God, you're all right! We were worried sick, but Seth did see

Andrew Cunningham coming for you, and he assured me that you had made it in from the storm.''

''We're fine, thanks,'' Katie murmured. She slid into the seat beside Susan and smiled at the other person at the table, a dark-haired woman probably closer to forty than thirty, very slim but with a smile and bright green eyes that made her attractive.

''Katie, do you know Lucy?'' Susan asked her.

''We've never met,'' the woman said, stretching out a hand to Katie. ''Lucy Thomason. Your son is being an absolute doll, entertaining the girls.''

Katie laughed. ''He has his moments!''

''The girls adore him,'' Susan said.

''And Jordan loves adoration, so I'm sure they'll be fine,'' Katie said. If she had asked him to entertain a couple of little girls under normal circumstances, she was certain he would have done so—but he would have made a heck of a face at her. Things were different now. She was certain he'd be willing to go bike riding or throw a baseball around with just about anybody.

''Katie, what would you like to drink?'' Sophie asked her.

''What are my choices?''

''Well, we've got ice tea, cold beer and soda.''

Katie decided on tea again, it had been so good before. As Sophie brought her a glass and sat down at the table with the other women, Susan murmured, ''I wonder if I should go get the guys. They get busy on a project and forget that time goes by.''

"There's no hurry," Sophie said. "They're getting your house back into shape, right?" Susan nodded. "Let them work, then," Sophie suggested.

"Have you decided to stay for sure, then?" Lucy asked Susan.

Katie arched a brow at Susan. "Andrew offered to buy our place back," Susan told her. "He offered to give us what we paid—and we'd keep the insurance settlement, as well."

"What you paid?" Katie heard herself ask. "You paid Andrew for your house?"

Sophie laughed. "Of course, dear. You didn't know? Andrew is Hunnicunn Corporation. He's really gone above and beyond any realm of responsibility."

"And I loved the house," Susan was saying. "We're not leaving—I know it's going to be even better once it's repaired."

There seemed to be a ringing in her ears. The conversation was continuing all around her, and she felt as if ocean waves were pouring over her.

Andrew was Hunnicunn Corporation. He had pulled her out of the storm, all but given her his home.

Because he was the one who had built her own! The one that had caved in during the storm.

She could sue him. They could all sue him.

"Well, the thing of it is," Lucy was saying, "that there was nothing illegal about the roofs that came down—they just weren't made with the usual Hunnicunn quality of materials and workmanship."

Katie felt sick. Furious. She wanted to scream and throw things.

He had told her that he owed her. Everyone knew. She simply hadn't understood.

Then she heard his voice. Heard his laughter as he walked into Sophie's house with Seth Keogh. Sophie grinned and hurried out to the living room to offer them cold beers. Both men thanked her and accepted.

Seth came into the kitchen first, grinning broadly. "We finished the broken tiles in the bedroom and got the new screens put in," he told his wife, pausing behind her to hug her shoulders. "With the bed out of the spare room, we'll have a new bedroom by tomorrow."

"Wonderful!" Susan said. Katie looked across the kitchen at Drew leaning in the doorway, holding the cold bottle of beer. They must have been working hard. A little trickle of sweat was running down his forehead to his chin. Other than that he looked . . .

Perfect.

Tall, well-built, so good-looking. Andrew Cunningham. Hunnicunn Corporation. Affluent, sophisticated, the man with everything. The man she had been sleeping with.

The one she should have sued!

Katie stood up and felt his eyes on her.

She felt her tension grow.

"Thanks, Drew!" Susan said.

She was going to strangle him, Katie thought. He was frowning, staring at her, wondering what was wrong. "Sophie," she managed to say, "I've got to go check up on something myself. Don't wait for me. Get started. I'm not sure when I'm going to be back.''

She fled out the French doors and walked around the side of the house. She felt on fire, burning with fury, with humiliation.

She crossed the circle and burst in through her front door, leaned against it and stared at the devastation of her house.

"Katie!"

She felt the slam of his fist on the door behind her back and she didn't move.

"Katie, let me in!"

She didn't have any choice. He must have thrown his shoulder against the door because it opened. She spun around, fists clenched at her sides, ready to meet him.

He stepped in, staring at her.

"Katie—"

"You bastard!" she hissed. "You did all this—and then you used me!"

"Katie—"

She didn't know quite what had gotten into her, but she couldn't seem to control herself. It was an awful day. First the tears, and now...

She took a step forward, swinging out a hand that cracked like thunder across his face.

He stood dead still, barely breathing, eyes narrowing as he stared at her. "I didn't use you."

"I could sue you!"

"Sue me, then, Mrs. Wells. There was nothing done illegally in construction."

"It was done cheaply!"

"I don't have an explanation and I don't have an excuse. And if you remember correctly, you came into my bedroom that first night."

"You carried me."

"After you attacked me in the hallway," he said smoothly.

"Oh!" she cried. She grabbed for the closest thing she could find to throw.

It was a smashed picture frame.

He ducked as it hurtled his way. He hesitated and Katie found herself breathless, scrambling backward to escape him as he came toward her. Before she knew it, she was in his arms. They were powerfully wound around her, and even as she struggled, he kissed her, furiously, passionately, openmouthed, arousing her against her will even as she struggled to be free. She was losing her breath, losing her will to fight...

His mouth lifted from hers and his eyes blazed down upon her. "I never, never used you!" he said. Then he released her. "Sue me!"

He turned and walked out, leaving her in her devastated living room. Speechless, gasping for breath. Not at all sure of what to do.

The door slammed after him. She paused, trying to still her nerves, trying to think. She had to go back for Jordan. She had to be calm and dignified, and she had to thank Sophie, and she had to eat dinner. Then what? She had her car. She needed to drive away.

She needed a night somewhere to collect herself. To decide if...

If she hated Drew Cunningham or if she was in love with him.

"I do hate you!" she told the door.

Then she bit her lip. She had to go to Sophie's. She didn't want Jordan to realize that anything was wrong.

She threw open the door and saw a silver gray Cadillac driving up to her house.

Her heart sank. Oh, God . . .

Her father was here. Even as she stood there, Ron Wheeler stepped out of the car, tall, slim, lean, gray-haired, dignified and handsome.

And ready to step right into her life.

"Katie!"

Chapter 8

For such a slim, dignified man, he packed a wallop in a hug. Katie was nearly swept off her feet, but then she found herself hugging her father with the same fierce affection. She loved him and she was glad to see him.

And she should have known he couldn't stay away!

He pushed her an arm's length from himself, looking her over. "Well, you seem fine. The house looks as if it's been through a blender, but you look all right, and that's what matters. Where's my grandson?"

"Across the street. We're having a party."

Her father lifted a gray, arched brow. "A party?"

"Well, my neighbors invested heavily in lobster tails—then lost their freezer. Well, not their freezer, but the electricity."

She saw Sophie coming out on her porch to look around.

Before the storm, Katie hadn't been able to see Sophie's house from her own. Now, courtesy of Andrew, she had a clear view. She waved, knowing that Sophie was worried about her.

Sophie brightened quickly and started across the street.

Her father frowned at her. "If the party's over there, what are you doing here?"

The last thing she felt like doing was trying to explain any of it to her dad. "I don't know. I must have had a premonition or something that you might be driving up."

"You never were a good liar, Katie."

"Shh! Sophie is almost here."

"There you are, dear! I was starting to get worried," Sophie said. Katie tried hard to keep smiling.

Did she need to have *everyone* worried about her?

"Sophie, this is my dad, Ron Wheeler. Mrs. Sophie Hampton, Dad. She and her husband, Len, live right across the street."

Ron shook Sophie's hand. "Very nice to meet you. You're the party people, eh?"

"Yes, and we have plenty, so do, please, come along!" Sophie said. Ron grinned a little wickedly at his daughter. Almost like, *See, I'm invited to your party, too!*

Katie made a face at him behind his back. Neither he nor Sophie noticed. "Sounds wonderful. Thank you," Ron said. "It's been a horrible drive down.

Broward County doesn't look great, and right after you pass it, it starts to look as if bombs went off.''

''I haven't braved the roads yet, myself,'' Sophie said, ''but I hear that driving is just horrible! But you're here, now. Come on over, relax, have something cool—and some of my husband's wonderful lobster.''

''That's very nice. Thank you. Katie?''

''Lobster,'' she said cheerfully. The three of them headed across the street, Katie in the rear while Ron and Sophie talked. Ron told Sophie that he'd spent most of his life in South Florida, but had gone up to the Orlando area to act as a consultant for a management firm, and that he'd wound up staying there. By then, they'd reached the house, and when they entered, Sophie had Ron on her arm, bringing him through the house and out the kitchen to the back, where the neighbors had fixed their plates with lobsters, fruit salad and chips.

Within a minute, Sophie had supplied Ron with a beer and was introducing him. ''Everyone, this is Katie's dad, Ron Wheeler, down from Orlando. Ron, let's see—there are the Thomasons, there's Mr. Ted Barlow, a great cribbage player, Susan, Seth and Amy Keogh, Midge and Brandon Holloway.'' Brandon rose from the picnic table at the end of the patio to shake hands with Ron. When he sat, Katie saw Drew standing just behind him.

''You're Andrew Cunningham,'' Ron said, stepping forward, reaching out a hand.

Katie stared at her father, wondering how he could be such a traitor. But Ron didn't seem to notice her. "I saw your picture in that magazine just a couple months ago. It was a great article on the art of building."

"Thank you," Drew said.

"Katie's been staying with Drew," Sophie supplied cheerfully.

"Oh." Ron said, turning to stare speculatively at his daughter. Katie wondered if he'd heard right—Sophie had said *staying,* not *sleeping*.

"Thanks on behalf of my daughter."

"You don't need to thank him, Dad," Katie said lightly. "He built my caved-in house. He feels that his is mine at the moment, isn't that right, Mr. Cunningham?"

Drew gazed at her before responding to Ron Wheeler smoothly. "I certainly consider it open to anything Katie needs, sir. Will you be staying with us tonight, as well?"

"No!" Katie said.

"Yes, if you don't mind," Ron Wheeler told him.

"But you came to get me, Dad—"

"And I thought you were anxious to stay," Ron said. "I'm assuming you're running around photographing everything in sight. And keeping an eye on your home, too, of course."

"Gramps!"

Jordan, who had been playing ball with the girls in the grass, realized that his grandfather had come. He came rushing in like a quarterback with the ball and threw himself into his grandfather's arms.

Katie was glad her father was still a strong man and in good health. He cried out happily, lifting Jordan up, swinging around with him.

He set him down and tousled his hair. "You look great, kid. I miss you. I was worried sick."

"It was scary, Gramps, really scary!" Jordan assured him. "Mom and I almost died—"

"Jordan—"

"But Drew came along and everything has been just fine!" Jordan assured his grandfather.

Ron arched a brow at Katie. "I told you that you should have been up in Orlando with me, young lady. Now as to this bit about the two of you nearly dying—"

"Dad, we're all fine, and everyone's lobster is getting cold," Katie said. "Len, may I have a plate? They look wonderful. They smell divine."

"Careful, Katie. They'll put you in the campaign ads for Maine lobster," Drew said, his tone light, his eyes sharp.

She inhaled deeply. A few minutes later, she found herself seated across from Drew at a picnic table, her father on one side, Sophie on the other, and Jordan and Len on either side of Drew.

She didn't think she'd ever get through the meal. Her father discussed with Drew everything he had seen on television about the building codes, about the way homes should be able to stand up to the wind.

"But steel girders were twisted in some places," Len said. "If steel can twist..."

"Some things were going to go down no matter what," Drew said evenly. "Some things didn't have to go down."

They had Sterno coffee and the no-bake dessert, and though they were in their own private cul-de-sac, there was a curfew on, and the neighbors began to break up and go to their own houses.

Ron Wheeler went to pull his overnight case out of his car, and when he returned, their foursome walked the short distance across the lawns to Drew's house.

"Grandpa can bunk with me," Jordan supplied as they came in. "It's a great house, Gramps. Want a tour?"

"Don't forget," Katie reminded her son, "it's Mr. Cunningham's house."

"Ah, but don't worry. Your mother agrees that I do owe it to her, so Jordan, roam where you will."

Jordan started up the stairs with his grandfather, and Katie was left staring at Drew at the foot of the stairs. His eyes were level with hers. She doubted her right to be furious.

But he hadn't told her. He'd built her damned house, and even according to him, it shouldn't have gone down. And he'd let all that time go by without saying anything. He'd made love to her...

She started to brush by him. He caught her arm.

"We'll go in the morning," she told him.

"You do what you have to do," he told her icily. His fingers eased their hold. Katie walked past him.

Somehow, she managed to tell her son and her father a cheerful good-night. Maybe she was lucky her dad had come. She might have been afraid—of herself or Drew, she wasn't certain—if she had come back here with just Jordan.

And at that time of night, there truly wasn't anywhere else to go. People were saying there wasn't a hotel room to be had for two hundred miles.

Upstairs, in her room—his room—she lay awake for hours, trying to reason things out. Nothing illegal had been done, and yet it hadn't been right. But the other neighbors weren't angry with him at all, and from what her father said, she would lose her case if she did try to sue him, since nothing he—or his corporation—had done had been illegal.

And maybe she didn't want to be angry with him. Maybe she didn't want to lie on sheets that still carried the slightest hint of his masculine scent. Maybe she'd been so in love with the idea of being in love that she couldn't think anymore.

In Drew's code of building, *quality* building, it had been wrong. So what had happened? Was he guilty of wanting to make more and more money?

And if not him . . .

Then perhaps someone was playing games behind the corporate back.

The thoughts revolved in her mind.

She stared at the hidden door that separated the rooms when she heard Drew enter his room. She tensed and waited.

But the door didn't open. She waited and waited. Ready to fight, dying to be persuaded. But he didn't come. It seemed that she sat up, in misery, forever.

Sometime, though, she must have slept. When she woke up, light was streaming into the room. Jordan was standing over her.

"Gramps is downstairs having coffee. He says he takes it that you want to leave today, so we'd best get started in the next few hours."

"Where's—Mr. Cunningham?" she asked.

"Drew has gone to his office," Jordan said. His voice was reproachful.

Even her child was on the man's side.

"He left a note, saying that he probably wouldn't be back and that we should have a nice drive and take a hot shower for him somewhere along the line."

Katie rose slowly. Her head hurt. She slipped into a robe and went downstairs.

Her father was at the breakfast table, watching the little television, sipping coffee. "Morning," he told her.

"Morning," she said.

"Wonderful house."

"Wonderful." Katie started to pick up her coffee cup.

"So what's going on between you and Drew Cunningham?"

She almost dropped her cup. "He's given us a place to stay since our house is a wreck," she said simply.

"Katie, I'm getting old, not stupid."

"Dad!"

"Great house. Good man. Seems like a shame you're just going to hand him over to some other woman."

"Dad, I get the impression that he has plenty of women in stock—just like copy paper—for any contingency." She was not ready for her father's advice—or tormenting. "I'll clean up and pack. Orlando will be great, after all. Hot water, air-conditioning. I can't wait."

"You won't be getting anything but tourist pictures up there," Ron said.

She paused a moment. "Dad, I took at least fifteen rolls, thirty-six exposure, of the storm damage. I think I covered most of it. Drew brought me around."

"The cad!" her father exclaimed.

"Oh, stick your nose in a coffee cup!" Katie told him, and hurried out of the kitchen as Jordan was unhappily wandering in.

But as she dressed, Katie decided that she couldn't leave things the way they were. She'd been about to slip into bike pants and a tank top, but she hesitated, then slipped into a knit dress instead. Taking only her purse, she hurried downstairs.

"I've got a quick errand to run," she told her father.

Ron had the *Reader's Digest* open before him. "You know where his corporate offices are?" he asked her.

Katie set her purse down with a sigh, a smile on her lips. "No, Dad. Where are they?"

He turned. "Right on the highway."

Jordan stood. "Can I come, Mom? I want to say goodbye and thanks to him."

"I'll go for the ride, too, Katie," Ron offered quickly, "and Jordan can keep me occupied if you need to talk about—about the house or anything."

His office was only ten minutes away—even in after-Andrew traffic—a large, white, modern, beautifully designed building. To the left, construction had apparently been going on before the storm. On the third floor, glass had been shattered out of the reflecting windows, and naked girders stretched out into the sunlight.

A receptionist in the center of the first floor called upstairs, and then they were allowed up to the third floor and the executive offices, where they were asked to wait once again.

Katie looked around. The office was impressive. The foyer floors were marble. Soft neutral carpeting covered the desk areas, and the long, broad reflecting window looked out on the day.

The hum of generators could be heard, keeping lights and business machines in action.

Katie's father suddenly stood up and asked the receptionist if there was anywhere to buy coffee. She directed him downstairs. "Tag along with me, Jordan. We'll be back up in enough time to say goodbye and thanks."

Katie looked at her father. He winked. She wanted to hit him.

Ron and Jordan disappeared down the stairway and she was left in the waiting area by herself.

A few minutes later, a striking redheaded woman, looking absurdly cool and fashionable despite the sticky weather, came toward the desk, a portfolio beneath her arm. "Is he in?" she asked the receptionist.

"I've just beeped him," the young woman said. "Jeannie says he's in the building somewhere, but he hasn't appeared yet."

He appeared right then. Striding down the hall, unrolling the sleeves of his tailored shirt. He didn't see Katie at first. He saw the redhead, and he smiled and whispered something soft as he touched her arms and kissed both her cheeks.

Katie felt like a spoke sticking out of a wheel.

"Mr. Cunningham," the receptionist said, "there's a Mrs. Wells to see you."

He spun around, seeing Katie. His eyes narrowed, his features tensed.

"Ah, Mrs. Wells! To what do I owe the honor?" he asked.

Katie grated her teeth together. "Jordan wanted to say thank you," she lied.

To her surprise, the redhead gasped and came toward her. "Hi, you must be Katie Wells. I'm Reva Kennedy," she said, very much as if Katie should know her.

"My sister, Reva Kennedy," Drew said.

"He didn't tell you he had a sister?" Reva said, arching a brow. "Ouch!" she told Drew. "Well, he told us a great deal about you. I'm so sorry about your house. And we're all stunned, of course, and we will get to the bottom of what happened. Not that a lot might not have been destroyed anyway, but our roofs are supposed to be among the best in the country!''

Katie stood, taking Reva's eager hand. "It's very nice to meet you." She smiled pleasantly at Drew. "There was a great deal your brother chose not to share with me," she said sweetly.

"He hasn't that much family left," Reva told her. "He should mention us now and then. Drew—these are some sketches I'd like you to look at. I'll leave you two to your business, but beware! It's a family day." She winked at Katie. "Mom is downstairs with the twins. She wants to say hi, since she hasn't seen you in person since the storm. We both live in West Palm so we came out of it all fine," Reva explained to Katie. "It was so nice to meet you. Drew, we were hoping to go to lunch, but I don't mean to interrupt anything—"

"You won't be," Katie said hastily. "I have to leave. We're going to Orlando for—for awhile. My father's home is there."

"Maybe you could join us for lunch before you leave. A number of the restaurants just to the north have opened again today. Places that have gotten their electricity back, or places that have good generators. Anyway, I know we'll find something good. Be warned, though. I have three-year-old twins."

Katie smiled at her. "Three-year-olds are no threat to me, but I'm afraid we need to get on the road. Knowing how traffic is, you'll understand."

"Ah, well, then..." Reva smiled at them both, waved and started for the stairway after placing her portfolio in her brother's hands.

Drew still didn't look in the least pleased to see Katie. "My office is just down here," he said, directing her to the left hallway.

Katie stepped ahead of him, nearly feeling his breath at her nape as he followed behind her. But when she entered his office—a pleasant, spacious place with a patterned sofa, dark wood desk, a conference table, numerous swivel chairs and floor-to-ceiling windows—he leaned against the door while she walked on in and stared out the window.

"You have something to say?" he asked her.

"I told you—"

"Right. Jordan wanted to see me. Well, where is he?"

"With Dad, trying to get a Coke or coffee or something. He'll be up immediately. Although actually..."

"Yes?"

She shrugged. "I wanted to—perhaps I judged you just a little bit too harshly."

"Really?" he murmured. He still seemed angry.

Hurt? she wondered. She swallowed hard. "Well, you are the damned builder of the house! And you didn't tell me—"

"Everyone else knew."

"I never had occasion to know!" Katie said angrily.

He was silent a moment, watching her. "If this is an apology, it isn't good enough."

"What?" she gasped.

"Maybe you're not quite as much at fault as I thought you were!" he said, imitating the style of her speech rather well. "Just what are you mad at, Katie? The house? Or your own insecurity in yourself? Five years is a long time to be alone."

"It's not so long when you see what happens when you aren't alone!" Katie retorted swiftly. She had been foolish to come. She couldn't tell if he hadn't been that emotionally involved from the beginning, or if she had angered him so much he didn't care about her anymore.

"Katie—" he began, but he broke off as there came a determined tapping at his door. He frowned, stepping away from it, and it opened to admit a slim, tiny woman with beautiful silver-gray hair, bright green eyes and one cute little redheaded boy in her arms and another by the hand.

Jordan was standing right behind her, and Ron Wheeler, his hands on his grandson's shoulders, was behind Jordan.

"Hi!" the woman said to Drew, starting to set the toddler down to give Drew a quick kiss and hug. Then she stepped across the room, offering a hand to Katie. "You must be Katie—your father has just been telling me all about you, although of course, I'd met Jordan over the phone before. How nice to meet you. We're so sorry, dear, about everything that has happened. I know that Drew will get to the bottom of it."

"My mother, Tina Cunningham," Drew said, the exasperation in his voice well masked.

"It's very nice to meet you," Katie said. She glanced over the woman's shoulder to see her father grinning like the Cheshire cat.

"We should probably be on our way," Katie began.

"Oh, but your father said it would be fine to have lunch with us, that you'd have plenty of time to get on the road," Tina said.

Katie narrowed her eyes at her father, who lifted his hands innocently.

"Mom, Gramps said we could. And Reva said that I'm great with her kids. They may be little, but at least they're boys this time!"

"Really," Katie said, "we wouldn't want to intrude."

"But, Mom—" Jordan said.

"It's lunch, Katie, just lunch," Drew said.

She wondered if anyone else could hear that he was speaking through clenched teeth.

She lifted her hands. "Fine."

In a few minutes, they were all leaving the office. The twins were Sean and Cameron, and they were very well behaved for being such little urchins, and surprisingly articulate, but Tina told Katie that they were almost four and went to a wonderful nursery school where they were taught while they played.

They met Reva at the foot of the stairs, and she seemed very pleased to see that Katie and her family had agreed to go.

"We'll need two cars," Ron said to Tina, as if they were the social organizers for a club. "Where should we head?"

"I know a place in South Miami that's very comfortable and family oriented, and they've just reopened today," Tina told him. "Just follow me."

As they started across the parking lot, a little Lotus drove in.

A woman exited from the car, unfolding her model's length with startling sensuality. She was tall, slim, shapely, and wearing a short skin-tight dress that would have been too much on anyone else—but on her it seemed to add to the sexy appeal. Her hair was long, parted at the side, nearly white-blond.

"Drew!" she called. She walked forward anxiously, hugged him, kissed him. Not on the cheek. On the lips.

Katie wasn't sure what Drew's reaction was to the woman.

She was only certain that the blonde wasn't another sister.

They had all paused, she realized. Every one of them—including the suddenly silent twins. And they were all staring at Drew and the blond woman.

He spoke to her softly. She spun around and waved. "Hi, Tina, Reva! Did you all make out okay?"

"Just fine," Tina called back.

"We were on our way to lunch," Katie heard Drew say. "But I do have to talk to you."

"Would you like to join us?" Tina asked politely.

The blonde laughed softly. "No, thanks. You've got quite a party with you already. I'm much better at . . . smaller affairs. Drew, I'll be here for a while," she said, and breezed past, into the offices. Drew followed his sister to her car, apparently unaware that the blonde had caused a stir. "I'll drive," he told Reva, taking her keys.

Katie slid into the passenger's side of her father's car. She was silent and tense as they drove, wanting to yell at her father . . . But not in front of her son.

"Wow! That was some . . . girl," Jordan said.

"Woman," Ron corrected.

"And not his sister," Katie murmured.

Her father shot her a quick glance. He arched a brow. "Chicken, kid?" he asked her.

"Dad, you don't begin to understand—"

"I'm your father. I don't want it spelled it out," Ron said. "Where'd they go?"

Katie pointed into the right lane. "We just had to go to lunch, huh?"

"I just met the most stunning widow I've come across in ten years!" Ron told her. "Play along, give me a break."

"What?"

Her father looked at her. "She's beautiful. She's pure energy. She's . . . charming."

"Oh, God!" Katie leaned back against the seat.

But lunch wasn't horrible at all. In fact . . . if Drew still didn't have gold daggers in his eyes every time he stared at her, she would have had a nice time. The twins behaved very well, and they were just as cute as could be. Jordan amused them and seemed to take great pleasure every time he had them laughing.

The restaurant was blessedly cool. The electricity had come back on; the staff was enthused, and the customers were all delighted. It was loud inside, but the decor—checked tablecloths and white napkins and wicker-strung wine bottles—was pleasant and laid-back.

Ron sat next to Tina. Their silver heads were often close. They laughed constantly.

Katie was next to Reva and across the circular table from Drew. She felt his stare often, but he seemed quiet.

Reva did most of the talking. She knew about Katie's photographs and seemed very intrigued. Then she began to explain her involvement in Hunnicunn. "We really had no choice but to know a great deal about building." Her voice grew a bit husky. "My dad was a great guy. He was in the construction field, and Drew and I used to tag alongside him when we were kids. I'm one of the few wives who really knows a good dovetail roof when she sees one! I married right out of college, and we traveled a great deal—my husband was military—and when we came back, we knew we wanted to start a family. But I really love architecture, and I'm incredibly lucky that Drew has his own corporation, so I get to design houses and sometimes he uses them and sometimes we modify them." She looked at Drew. "Have you found anything out yet?" she asked him.

"No," he said flatly, firmly.

Reva shrugged. "I've been trying to figure it out. Giles would never have done a roof so cheaply. Do you know Giles?" she asked Katie.

"Yes, I've met him."

"Well, sometimes, of course, we have to subcontract. But I still can't figure out such a work order. I've been trying to think about who in the corporation has the kind of power to change what's already on paper. Mom's signature would never be questioned, but then, she has never touched a single design of ours and why would she do so? Then there's Andrea, of course. She's not much on actual work, but she is the only Hunnington left in Hunnicunn."

"Andrea?" Katie heard herself say.

"The blonde at the office," Reva said.

"Oh," Katie murmured. She found herself staring at Drew again. He was staring back at her.

"Me, Mom, Drew. Then there's Sam, sweet old Sam, and Harry—who's even older and sweeter. They both worked with Dad, and they were very good, so they're still with Drew. I just can't begin to figure—"

"Reva," Drew said, stepping firmly into the conversation. "I spoke with Giles—he checked the records. It's my signature on the work order."

"But, Drew—"

"Reva, it's my problem, and I'm going to deal with it."

"Well, of course," Reva told Katie, "the Hunnicunn offer remains out on all our homes. We pay back the price of them and the owners pocket their insurance, as well. You could double your investment on your house. Of course, you never get back the sentimental things that are lost, but then—"

"Thousands of people don't even have clothing!" Ron Wheeler said, suddenly speaking up from his end of the table. "Katie and Jordan came out of it okay."

"How did you get out when your house collapsed?" Reva asked, shivering.

"We—ran," Katie said.

"Yeah, it was terrible!" Jordan said, passing the catsup to one of the twins. "Mom tripped over a banyan. We wouldn't have made it if Drew hadn't come along."

Katie clenched her teeth. Drew let out an exclamation of impatience.

"I *was* lucky," Katie admitted, "that your brother came out when he did."

"Thank God all around!" Tina said. "And you just wait. Things will come back around again."

"Mom, you haven't seen Cutler Ridge. Or Homestead," Drew said quietly.

"I saw a T-shirt the other day," Tina said, smiling. "It read, We Will Rebuild. And people will. Don't forget, they pulled this area out of the swamps and marshes from the very beginning. Killer storms have come and gone before. Some people will leave, sure. But some will rebuild. It's just part of the human spirit. We learn. We grow."

"I learned I sure do miss Nintendo," Jordan said, and they all laughed. Even Drew and Katie smiled.

Until they looked at one another. And she couldn't help but think that Andrea Hunnington might be another factor in Drew's life that he had forgotten to mention.

Lunch finally came to an end. Jordan sighed, eating a last french fry. "Boy, that was good!"

"I have to get back," Drew said, looking at his watch after he and Ron had argued over the check and Drew had managed to take it.

"Well, then, I owe you one," Ron told him.

"I don't think Katie feels much in debt, sir," Drew said lightly, but he paused to ruffle Jordan's soft blond hair. "Bye, Jordan. I'll miss you. I'm sorry you didn't get a chance to use the setup in your room. Maybe another time."

Jordan didn't speak. He swallowed hard.

"Thank you again," Katie managed to say. She had wanted to sound more sincere. Her voice was cold. Was he right? Was she too insecure to believe in herself?

Suddenly, it didn't seem to matter. Her chances were over.

They were out of the restaurant, and she found herself shaking hands with Drew, politely, courteously saying goodbye. To a stranger.

In their separate cars, they drove in opposite directions. Andrew heading south. Katie, her father and her son heading north.

And two hundred miles later, surrounded by air-conditioning, staring at the crystal-clear water in Ron's pool, she felt hot tears prick against her eyes.

She had just driven hundreds of miles away from the first real happiness she had known in years. And now . . .

Now it was lost, as so much else that had been lost in the tempest of Andrew.

We Will Rebuild...

It was a motto for a devastated county. And she knew she would go back, that she would rebuild. It was home; she loved it.

She only hoped she could rebuild what she had begun with Drew the same way as she would her home, step by step...

Chapter 9

A week passed easily enough at her father's house—naturally, everything was normal here, and there were numerous things to do to keep herself and Jordan busy.

Jordan didn't have to be back to school until the following Monday, since half the schools couldn't open. He wound up with a very special extended vacation as they toured the Orlando sights, going from Disney World to Universal Studios, Typhoon Lagoon and Sea World.

Katie tried to beg out of the excursions; her heart just wasn't in them. But her father and her son plagued her into coming, and Ron constantly put in a few little digs referring to her relationship—or lack of one—with Drew.

If she hadn't felt so mercilessly tormented, she would have had a good time. She loved her father and his home. He had bought it with her and Jordan in mind, and she had a beautiful room with clothes in the closet and a supply of shoes. She sent Midge's shoes back to her, and with a gift certificate and a thank-you note as well.

She swam, she grew tan. She took very hot showers, and luxuriated in air-conditioning that was on full blast.

She spent hours wondering about Drew, about what had happened. She remembered listening to Reva and counting the people in Drew's office who might have the power to change plans and orders.

But his signature had been on the work order. So no one would have questioned it. So...

Ah, well. There were two mystery men, the older men who had worked with the father. There was Drew himself. There was Reva and their mother. And then there was Andrea...

Katie wanted Andrea to have done something very slimy and underhanded. But why? She obviously had plenty of money, why try to get more?

Why, indeed. Many people wanted more and more, Katie reflected. Greed was a human emotion. And, of course, Katie wanted Andrea to be very greedy.

Evil, even!

She wondered what Andrea had said to Drew when he had returned from lunch. Katie tortured herself with pictures of the blonde in Drew's bedroom, in the guest room, waiting for Drew as he opened the hidden door between the rooms...

I've walked out! she reminded herself. She'd told him what she thought of him, and she'd walked out. Then she'd tried to apologize, and he hadn't listened.

Maybe she hadn't apologized with tremendous sincerity, but she'd had the right to doubt him!

On the eighth day of her visit, Katie awoke to find the house silent. She showered, threw on a robe and entered the kitchen to find a note from her father. "Katie, gone out, will be back late, have Jordan, Love, Dad."

"Well, that's lovely. Where did you go?" she murmured, reaching for the coffeepot. She poured herself a cup and turned to walk to the living room.

She nearly screamed aloud. She went dead still, barely keeping the coffee cup from crashing to the floor.

Drew was here. He was seated in her father's easy chair reading the Orlando *Sentinel.* He set it down and stood, hands clasped behind his back. He was in blue jeans that hugged his hard thighs and long legs and a red knit shirt that enhanced the muscle structure of his arms and chest. His hair was neatly combed back, and his face was bronze, as if he'd spent a great deal of time outdoors since she had seen him.

Her heart flip-flopped and the wildest dance of fire seemed to snake down her spine. She was amazed by the sensations that swept through her.

Where on earth was something within her that resembled pride?

"What—are you doing here?" she asked him. "In the house. How did you get in?"

He arched a brow. "You didn't know that your father asked my mother to visit?"

"What?"

He shrugged. "Your father asked my mother up for a few days."

"And you—you're staying, too?" she asked, a strange panic seizing her.

He didn't answer. He kept staring at her, gold eyes hard, unforgiving. She longed to have her father in front of her then. She'd like to shake him like a rag doll. What did he think he was doing to her? Drew had people like Andrea in his life—perfect people.

And here was Katie, clean but sodden.

Sodden seemed to be the way he saw her most often.

No makeup. Her hair was still damp from her shower, curling around her squeaky-clean face. And she was well-dressed again, as well. This time, a worn velvet robe.

Maybe she hadn't spoken loudly enough.

"Are you—are you staying, too?"

"No, I have to go back. I won't be able to leave home for at least a month. I'm a builder—in case you forgot, which I'm sure you didn't."

There was bitterness in his tone.

She inhaled. Maybe she should try apologizing again. Maybe she was a fool. Maybe he had said good riddance to her and rushed back to receive another kiss from his partner's daughter.

"Why—are you here?" she asked.

"To see you."

"If you're going to try to explain—" she began, but she broke off. He was striding across the room to her, and she found she couldn't speak. Her coffee mug was plucked from her fingers and set down.

"I didn't come to explain anything," he told her.

"Then—"

Her voice was cut off as he roughly took her into his arms.

"Drew—" she began, but his mouth crushed down on hers with amazing force and coercion. Her lips parted beneath the power, and a rush of heat seemed to come with the liquid fire of his kiss and sweep its way through her. She struggled against him only briefly, then forgot why she might protest. His hands were suddenly within her robe, on her naked flesh, rising and falling along her rib cage, rising to caress her breasts, falling to stroke her abdomen while he pressed her against the wall. His mouth remained passionately on hers, kissing her until her knees grew weak. His lips parted from hers as he inhaled deeply, and Katie managed to murmur, "I still don't understand what—what you're doing here. If you have to leave—"

"I'd thought I'd stay to remind you of what you were missing," he said huskily, his lips a breath away from her own.

"Of all the conceited—"

"I'm the best thing you've had in a long, long time," he told her, eyes blazing, body pressing hers hard against the wall. She could feel all the searing heat within him, the fullness of his arousal, the excitement he sent burning into her wherever he touched.

"Of course," he added softly, "I'm the only thing you've had for a long, long time, but still the best."

"Drew—" Too late. His lips were on hers, sweeping away words and thoughts. She found herself in his arms, and he was moving down the hallway, his eyes pinioning hers.

"Which door?" he demanded. "Here?"

"No." She shouldn't be telling him, she thought vaguely. He thought he could just walk right in here and . . .

"Next door," she murmured.

In a matter of seconds they were in her room in her father's house, the velvet robe on the floor along with his shirt. The air-conditioning seemed cool against the simmering heat of their bodies, against his touch, against the fevered kisses he rained down on her body. She kissed his shoulders, teased his earlobe, stroked her fingers down the length of his back . . .

Drawing them around to his front.

He rose, shedding sneakers, socks and jeans, and when she was in his arms again, she found herself being laid back into the pillows and hearing his whisper in her ear.

"I'm here to remind you of what you're missing," he told her again. Then she felt his lips on her throat, her breasts, her lips again. His hands were magic, moving over her with a fiery, caressing touch that tantalized.

His lips followed every touch. His wet, heated kisses touched her flesh. The air cooled them. She felt his fingers, teasing, sliding within her, and she tried to crawl against him, to touch him in return. He rose above her briefly.

"I want you to remember what you're missing," he said huskily, and no matter how she writhed, she found herself beneath him again, found his kisses following his most intimate touch, sending her into an absolute frenzy.

The sweet agony of longing he so intimately created was almost more than she could bear when he rose once again, staring at her long and hard as he drove himself deeply within her.

"Remember?" he asked softly.

Her fingers laced around his neck and her head tossed on the pillow as he began to move and she moved with him. Sun streamed in from the floor-length windows bathing them both in its golden light. She closed her eyes, desperately feeling the sweet buildup of excitement within her, holding him, clinging to him...

Remembering. His lips found hers. His tongue gently savaged her mouth while his body demanded everything from hers. She felt the sudden, wild tension of his body, the spill of liquid fire from within him, and that sent her spiraling to her own sweet pinnacle, trembling, falling then, falling ever so slowly while the pleasure stayed and simmered within her, remaining as a golden glow even when the last of her tremors had faded away. She felt his fingers, tenderly caressing her nape, pulling her against him.

"I've really missed you," he said softly.

"I've missed you," she admitted. "But then I've been here with Dad and Jordan, and you've been dealing in company business with your—partner."

He frowned, moving away from her, staring into her eyes. "Andrea?" he said.

"Miss Hunnington."

He smiled. Pleased. "You were jealous of Andrea?"

"Not jealous—merely aware."

He shrugged. "Well, she's the last person you should be jealous of."

"Why?"

"I don't like her. I never have."

"But she's very attractive."

"But I don't like her."

Katie felt her lashes fall, and a little thrill she couldn't resist fluttered in her stomach. He was telling the truth.

Yet just when she was feeling that secret happiness, he rose, walked to the windows and looked out at the beautiful yard with its turquoise pool and private shrubbery.

Then he stepped into his briefs and jeans and pulled his shirt over his head.

He walked to the bed, stooped and kissed her forehead.

"Were you glad to see me?" he asked, a wicked tone in his voice.

"Perhaps," she said warily.

"Good."

"Perhaps not," she warned.

He straightened, arching a brow. "Well, you'll have to decide on that. Because I really have to go. If you want more of this morning—of me, to be precise—you'll just have to come home."

"Why, you—!" Katie gasped, inching up on the bed to stare at him incredulously. "Conceited butthead!" she charged him, borrowing one of Jordan's words since she couldn't seem to find her own.

He smiled, then sobered. "I never meant any ill to you, Katie. I never meant to use or betray you in any way. And if you were outraged that I might be angry with you, remember this. You didn't trust me. You didn't give me a chance."

"Wait! You have no right—"

"I've got to go. It's a long ride back. When you can't stand it anymore, come home."

He turned and left the room. He didn't intend to wait for her—he didn't intend to give her a chance to say anything to him.

"It will be a cold day in hell!" she yelled after him.

She was surprised when his head popped in the doorway.

"It might be, at that. The heat down there is murder. Electricity is starting to come back on. See you, Katie."

And then he was gone. By the time she'd managed to tie her robe around her body, he had slipped out the front door, entered his Probe—and was driving down the street.

"Bastard!" Katie hissed beneath her breath, watching him go.

Then she was alone, and the air-conditioning seemed too cold.

She stepped out on the patio and sat down by the pool, trailing her feet in the water.

She believed in him, she knew. And she was in love with him. And if there was any way to let him know that she really did believe in him . . .

That way might be to find out who was behind the skimming of the profits at Hunnicunn Corporation.

Eliminate the impossible, her dad always told her, and what's left, whether improbable or not, has to be the truth.

All she had to do was find out what was impossible.

Maybe she had to find out more about Hunnicunn Corporation.

She was good at finding out about the past—it had always helped her with her photography. She'd always loved to pore through the microfilm at the library.

The day passed quietly. She drew charts with names of those involved, linking them all together. She'd have to find out a little something about them all. Andrea Hunnington. Her pencil kept circling that particular name. She reminded herself that she wanted to think of Andrea as evil, and maybe the woman was—Drew had said he didn't like her.

When she was hungry, she made herself a tuna sandwich and waited for her father, her son—and Drew's mother—to come home.

Her father's note had said that they'd be late—and he hadn't lied. Katie was convinced that her father had purposely left her alone with Drew as long as possible.

Even assuming Drew might have stayed for awhile, Katie thought with a certain warm amusement, they would never have needed this much time! But it was summer, and for the rest of untouched world, it was still vacation time, and the parks were open late.

Ron, Jordan and Tina came in just after midnight. Katie was sitting on the couch in the living room, still playing with her solve-the-mystery graphs when they trailed in. Jordan was yawning and her father and Tina Cunningham were smiling like a pair of kids themselves—and not appearing in the least bit tired.

"Katie!" her dad greeted her, leaning over to kiss her forehead. "Have a nice day? A good rest? Did you wake up before Drew had to leave?" he asked innocently.

"Yes, I did. But very briefly." She smiled at Drew's mother and told her father, "He was really in a big hurry. I'm not sure he stayed more than fifteen minutes."

"Oh," Ron Wheeler said. He sounded disappointed and puzzled.

Tina Cunningham seemed just as downcast.

"So—how was your day?" Katie asked.

"Jordan took us on Space Mountain. We were both nearly candidates for pacemakers," her father told her.

Katie laughed.

"Tina is great!" Jordan said, coming to life to extol the woman's virtues. "She went on it with me a second time!"

"Brave woman," Katie teased Tina.

"I've been dragged on worse before," Tina assured her. Katie smiled again and wished she didn't like Drew's mother so much.

It would be nice not to like *something* about her.

But Tina was warm and fun and seemed as open and above board as the daylight sun. Katie couldn't help but like her.

And it was obvious that her father more than liked her.

"Want coffee or tea or anything?" Katie asked. "Tina, can I get you anything you might be missing? Toothpaste, toothbrush—I'm not sure what kind of accommodations Dad arranged for you..." She let her voice trail off. The older crowd here seemed to like to put her in awkward positions. It seemed only fair play that she taunt them a bit in return.

But neither of them blushed or fell for the bait. "I'm quite fine, dear," Tina said.

Katie stood. "Well," she said sternly, "you two senior delinquents are going to be on your own as of tomorrow. I'm going to take Jordan and fly home. The week has been great, Dad, but there's just too much I need to take care of in Miami."

"Oh, you're going home?" her father said. He tried to sound disappointed, but there was that old light of mischief in his eyes. He wasn't sorry in the least. In fact, he seemed just as smug as the Cheshire cat.

"Yes, I'm going home. That okay with you, Jordan?" she asked her son.

"Hey. Sounds cool to me," Jordan said with a shrug.

"Well, then, good night, you all," Katie said, kissing Jordan's head and starting toward the hallway. "Jordan, we'll try to get a plane in the early afternoon, so you might want to get in bed soon. And Dad . . . well, you two behave."

Katie was halfway down the hallway when she heard Drew's mother say to Ron Wheeler, "Think we ought to tell her that I've got a hotel room?"

"Heck, no! Let her wonder!" Ron said.

Grinning, Katie went into her bedroom. But she didn't fall asleep right away, and later she heard a soft tapping at her door.

"Come in," she said.

Her father peeked in. "You up?"

She nodded and patted the side of her bed. He came in and sat beside her. "You really ready to go home?" he asked her. "Drew said most of the traffic lights are still out, though a lot of the roads have been cleared now. Things are getting better, but it will still be a while before they're good."

Katie nodded. "I think I need to be home, Dad."

"Drew have anything to do with that?"

"Maybe," Katie admitted. "But I think you're the one with the hot and heavy romance."

Ron chuckled. "Well, if so, I have you to thank for it."

"You don't need to thank me just because you met at Drew's office."

Ron shook his head. "I need to thank you for being stubborn and willful. See, Drew told Tina a little bit about you—enough for her to know something above the ordinary was going on. So I really got to know Tina when she very bluntly asked me if I'd persuade you to stay for lunch, but then that didn't work out so well. So I called her and suggested that maybe she could convince him that she was dying to come and see me, and then he might be willing to drive her up here. Then he'd have to see you."

Katie gasped. Ron shrugged.

"Dad! What a meddling old matchmaker!" she accused him.

"Well, now, I didn't make the match."

"Andrew made the match."

"The man? Or the storm?"

"A little bit of both," Katie said. And she frowned. "Dad, he didn't tell me right away that he was the architect and builder for my house. So when I found out . . ."

"You jumped straight to conclusions."

"Maybe," Katie admitted. "But, Dad, I'm going to try to find out what did happen. Maybe that can straighten everything out a little bit."

Ron shook his head, then his finger, at her. "Leave it to Drew, Katie. Stay out of it. If someone has been skimming big profits, he or she isn't going to want anyone finding out about it."

"Dad, I can be careful—"

"I won't let you go, Katie, if that's what you've got up your sleeve."

"Dad! I'm over thirty, remember?"

"Katie, promise me—"

"Dad, don't worry about me. I'm just planning on reading some newspaper files, nothing else. I'll give anything I can find to Drew, I promise."

"Be careful, Katie."

"I will be," she said.

"In every way," he warned her. "You know, you're like a babe in the woods now—"

"Mmm, and that's why you were throwing me to the wolf, you sly fox!" Katie said.

"I was just giving you a nudge. You've got to be careful."

"I will be, Dad."

"I'll keep in touch, and I'll be here whenever you need me."

"I know you will, and that's great." She hesitated, but he took her into his arms.

"Love you, baby," he told her.

"I love you, too, Dad. I love you, too. Maybe that's why it took me so long to think I needed anyone else again. I had a wonderful marriage, and I had you."

"Well, I'm trying to get a new woman in my life," he teased lightly, "so you go and see if you can get your man. He's a darned good one, too, I think."

"Why was I the only one without any faith?" Katie asked him.

"You were the one with the most to lose," he said. He stood. "Night, Katie," he told her.

She smiled. He left her room.

She slept amazingly well that night.

By one o'clock the following afternoon she and Jordan were boarding a plane that would take them to Miami International Airport.

The flight was smooth. Jordan seemed exceptionally lively and very anxious to get back.

"Aren't you going to miss Mickey Mouse?" she teased him.

"Sure, Disney is great. But so is home."

"We're not really going *home*," she reminded him. "We don't actually have a home anymore."

"It's still home," Jordan said determinedly.

He sat back, and they both enjoyed the flight. The weather was beautiful; the sky was an almost uncanny blue.

Katie got a cab from the airport. She had it take her and Jordan to Drew's house.

He didn't answer when she knocked. She tried the door and found it open.

"Think we should just go in?" Jordan said doubtfully.

Katie hesitated. "Yes," she said firmly. She brought in their luggage and set it in the hallway.

"Mom!" Jordan said suddenly. "There's electricity in here now!" And he was right. The air-conditioner was humming. A light was burning in the kitchen.

"I guess things are starting to get back to normal," Katie said. "Umm—bring your things up to the room you were using—"

"And I can use the Nintendo?"

"I guess. Just—"

"Keep things picked up, I know, it isn't our house, it's Drew's."

"Right. I'm going to get my bag out of the hall-way, too, smarty pants," she told him.

They started up the stairs, Jordan to his room and she to hers.

When she went in, the room seemed cast in shadows. She didn't know what she had been expecting. Yes, she did. She had thought he might be waiting for her. She was certain he had come home. She hoped fervently that she hadn't misread his message in Orlando...

No. He wanted her back. Things had to be said between them. She hadn't misunderstood him.

How could she have misread such a message?

She set her luggage on the bed, and it was only then that she noticed a note on the pillow.

She picked it up, read it and smiled.

"Welcome home, Katie," was all that it said.

It was enough.

Maybe she was home, after all.

She tried to wait up; it was easier with the electricity on and the house dark. But he hadn't come home by midnight, and she gave up trying to watch the late show.

She went up to her room to lie down, and despite her best efforts, she dozed.

She didn't know what awakened her, but she opened her eyes, blinking. He was there, in the doorway, a dark, still silhouette.

"Katie?" he said softly.

She ran across the room and was quickly wrapped in his arms.

"You came back," he said softly. "And—quickly."

"I had some really great memories of the place," she told him.

He laughed softly and swept her up.

And it was just like coming home.

Chapter 10

"Listen, it's my company, and I'll deal with it!" Drew said emphatically, slipping a knot into his tie.

Katie, her fingers curled around a mug at the breakfast table, clenched her teeth.

She should have kept quiet. She should have kept her mouth shut about what she wanted to do. Except that it would have been so much easier, and better, if he had been willing to help her. But he was so damned exasperating. He could be so charming one moment...

And so pigheaded the next.

"I was merely suggesting that I could help," she began.

"I don't want you to help."

"Drew—"

"Katie, I don't want your help!"

"But don't you think it's important to know exactly what happened?"

"Why? Do you have to prove it to yourself that I wasn't really to blame?"

"Drew!"

"Katie, I want you out of it, do you understand?" he demanded, his hands on the table as he leaned close to her.

"You have no right to tell me what to do," she said firmly.

"I have every right to tell you to get the hell out of my life and problems!"

That stung. She sat back, feeling almost as if he had struck her.

"Katie, I mean it."

She sat very stiffly, making her eyes stay level with his.

"Didn't you say that my house was nearly in a habitable condition?"

"Damn it, Katie, I didn't mean—"

"Maybe you could be so kind as to rush things along to the best of your abilities."

"Yeah," he said softly. "Maybe I can. But you don't need to worry. If you have any reservations about me at all, you can stay here and we can pass right by in the halls, lady, just like ships at sea. But you do what you want. Believe me, or don't believe me. I am at fault. Again, I'm telling you—sue me. You can even give your lawyer this address. The only thing you can't do is stick your nose into it!"

"You wretched bastard!" Katie hissed, rising. "You had me come back here—"

"To be with me, not run my life! You don't know Hunnicunn, you don't know the past, and you don't know what you might be up against. You don't know anything!"

"What might I be up against? Someone practicing fraud? I just want—"

"I don't give a damn what you want. I want you out of it! And if that means you're walking out of my house, well, then, you know the way!" He turned rigidly and stalked out of the kitchen. She would have raced after him and assured him that she would be out of his house just as quickly as possible, but she started shaking, and her knees were too weak to rise. She felt so damned vulnerable again. Afraid. She'd begun to feel so comfortable, so much a part of his life...

Cared for, if not cherished.

But he was right. She didn't know Hunnicunn. She didn't know him—she didn't know anything.

The front door had slammed long moments ago when she managed to get to her feet.

Jordan was at school. His first day. It seemed so strange. It had been wild getting there. The majority of the traffic lights remained down, and many of the roads were clogged with fallen trees. But the morning had also seemed filled with a certain charged tension—as if all of the community knew that the opening of the Dade County public school system meant that life was going on.

Katie swore at Drew under her breath, then grabbed her purse and let herself out the front door, locking it with the key he had given her.

Half the county was being looted, he had told her, and they couldn't leave his house open for any thief to walk right in. They'd been playing with a certain amount of danger before.

Well, she'd made sure his door was locked. And she would be out of it for good, just as soon as possible. If she and Jordan couldn't stay in her own home in the next few days, she'd find a hotel room—even if she had to find a filled one and empty its occupants into Drew's house!

But, no matter how angry and hurt she was, she realized a few minutes later, he hadn't changed her mind. He had no right to be so angry with her. It wasn't as if anyone had been murdered. Someone was embezzling money—it was a white-collar crime. She'd love to find the thief he'd been harboring beneath his own nose and hand the man—or woman—over to him. Dust off her hands...

Slap him a good one in the cheek...

And walk away. Heart and pride intact. Only her heart wasn't intact anymore.

She drove to the library, the main one, without caring about the traffic she had to confront to get there.

By eleven, she was ensconced before one of the microfilm machines.

At one o'clock, she was still staring at the microfilm, leafing back and forth through the pages she'd been able to find with references to Hunnicunn, the people involved with it—and Drew himself.

She stretched. She'd been at it a long time, her eyes and her back hurt and her head was beginning to ache.

And she hadn't found a thing.

Well, she'd found articles, but not what she'd wanted.

Fifteen years ago, Hunnicunn had been formed, and there had been an article on the corporation in the business section. There was a picture of a young Drew shaking hands with Henry Hunnington, a tall, slim man with thinning hair and an aging face. In the background were a number of people, a few Katie recognized, a few she didn't. Tina Cunningham was there, as was Reva. Katie also recognized a very young Andrea Hunnington. The two men on either side of Drew and Hunnington had to be Sam Jaffe and Harry Easton, but she didn't know which was which, and she didn't know if it mattered, except that one of them seemed familiar, the younger of the two, the darker one, only...

Only what, she didn't know.

She was going through a lot of years, she reminded herself. Looking for some kind of needle in a haystack.

She tried looking for information about Andrea, and that was abundant enough—in the society pages. The blonde had been married several times, but had always legally kept the name Hunnington. Her father had been involved in many enterprises, and it seemed she enjoyed the recognition of the name.

Each of her marriages had been chronicled. She was also present at all kinds of fund-raisers and the like.

There was nothing that hinted she might be trying to skim money from Hunnicunn.

Katie had decided to give up for the afternoon when she was startled to see the Cunningham name, front-page news. The story was almost twenty years old.

It was about the accident that had killed Drew's father.

A. J. Cunningham had been killed at a building site. He had fallen from the fifth-floor scaffolding he'd been working on. The fall had crushed his skull, killing him instantly.

She flicked through the paper and saw that the whole community mourned. There were pictures of a younger, darker Tina, with her two nearly grown children. Drew, striking even as a very young man, his handsome face twisted with anguish that tugged at her stomach.

There were pictures of the funeral. There were interviews with men A.J. had worked with, including Sam Jaffe and Harry Easton. Katie noted where A. J. Cunningham had been buried, and she thoughtfully turned off the screen.

She still didn't have anything.

She needed to think.

She left the library and drove through Little Havana, the Calle Ocho area, until the street was just plain old Eighth Street again, and she came upon Woodlawn Cemetery. The place was huge, and she had no idea where to find A. J. Cunningham's grave, but a trip into the caretaker's office gave her the directions she needed, and she drove through the cemetery, seeing older, traditional angels and monuments along with more modern memorials. Toward the rear of the cemetery she parked the car, certain she was in the right place. Under an old oak, the man had said. She peered at grave after grave, and then, staring across the cemetery, she was certain she had found the grave.

A. J. Cunningham had been laid to rest in a private mausoleum. It was sculpted to look like a sleek, beautiful home with Greek columns and a graceful porch. The name Cunningham had been chiseled over the columns, and Katie was certain a place remained within the mausoleum for Tina Cunningham to find her final rest.

She stood in front of the grave, feeling a breeze lift her hair.

''He's lying, you know!'' she told the structure, as if she could speak to the long-gone but deeply loved man. ''He's everything you might have wanted him to be, he's just afraid to let me in on this, and it doesn't make any sense. And he can get mad, and he can even throw me out if he wants, but I'm going to find out what happened!''

There was no answer. Had she gotten one, she probably would have had a heart attack on the spot. But the breeze remained nicely cool, the trees seemed to whisper, and she was somehow glad that she had come.

Then she began to feel a prickling sensation in her neck. As if she was being watched.

The breeze lifted the branches of the trees again. The grave was in a remote section of the cemetery, far from the main roads.

She might well be alone out here with...

She spun around, her heart pounding. Relief poured through her.

Reva Cunningham Kennedy was standing by her car, parked right in front of Katie's on the road.

Reva waited, watching as Katie walked over to her.

"My God, what a coincidence!" Katie murmured.

Reva shook her head. "No coincidence. You asked the caretaker about Dad. They had some vandalism here a few years ago and so they called the office. I was the Cunningham they managed to get hold of."

"So you came out to see what was going on?"

Reva shrugged.

"What if I had been a vandal?"

"And what if someone in my brother's corporation is dangerous?" Reva asked her in return.

Katie didn't answer. "Where are the twins?" she asked.

"Nursery school. Jordan?"

"His school opened today." She said awkwardly, "I know your brother is really angry with me over this, Reva, but I can keep my distance, and no one needs to know what I'm doing."

"What are you doing?"

"Nothing—really." She hesitated. "I just wish I knew everyone involved. I keep thinking that perhaps Andrea—"

"Andrea would be a prime suspect," Reva agreed with a certain amount of humour. "She's rich and gorgeous. And not terribly nice. But I'm not sure that's a crime."

"Well, it seems that everyone else is nice."

"And is what *seems* always real?" Reva asked her.

"Reva, help me," Katie said. "I swear to you, I want to do anything I can for Drew."

"And what if you find out that Drew is really guilty himself, that his lofty ideals are all lies?"

"They're not," Katie said.

"What if?"

"There is no what if!"

"All right," Reva said. "There's going to be a party in the office on Friday night. A thank-you from Drew to all the staff for working so hard since—since the other Andrew!"

"He'll never invite me," Katie said. "We've had quite a disagreement—"

"So I imagined," Reva said. "He walked into the office like a storm this morning. But he hasn't really said anything to me—he hasn't told me I can't invite you—so we'll just say that I wanted to ask you and Jordan since you're both so wonderful at helping me with the twins. You'll get to meet everyone, but Katie, I know he wants to keep you out of it. Don't you see, he's worried."

"Why?"

Reva shrugged. "Well, we are talking about a big money crime here. Katie, people shoot people to steal fifty dollars from fast-food stands."

"But no one ever needs to know what I'm up to!" Katie said. "Surely, *everyone* wants to know what happened!"

"My brother's signature was on the work orders for your house," Reva reminded her. "And nothing that was done was actually illegal."

"I know."

"Well, I don't know what the week will bring," Reva murmured, "but come to the office at five. I'll be sure to meet you before Drew sees that you're there."

"Thanks," Katie told her.

"You really get to help with the twins, you know!" Reva said, starting around to the driver's side of her car. "Mom used to be great, but... Well, she's off in Orlando, as you know."

Katie smiled. "I know. Thanks again, Reva. I'll see you Friday at five, and Jordan and I will both be ready to watch the boys."

Reva drove away.

Katie hesitated, then felt the breeze touching her arms, and she shivered.

The cemetery was remote.

And for some reason, she had chills.

She hurried to her own car and drove out.

Drew had seen to it that her house had been coming along while she had been gone. Her walls had been replastered, and new carpeting was down. Her bedroom had been repaired, but her windows remained boarded, since the new glass for them wasn't ready yet.

Her mangled screen had been pulled down, and some of the broken remnants of life that had blown into it had been removed from her pool.

After she picked up Jordan from school, she went to her house and stood in the doorway. She was still missing electricity. She had learned to manage without it, but...

The house was hot.

"We're going to stay here, now?" Jordan asked her.

"I guess not," she said after a minute.

"Please, not!" Jordan said.

Well, Drew had said that she could walk by him in his hallways, she reminded herself. And he hadn't asked her for his key or anything. She had been the one saying she meant to leave.

But he had been hostile.

He didn't mean it . . .

How could she be so sure when he *was* right about one thing? *She didn't really know anything, she didn't really know him* . . .

"Well, we'll go back to Drew's," she said. "But just for a few more nights, Jordan. We have to get back into our own house. We have to lead our own lives again."

"I've been incredibly neat!" Jordan said indignantly.

Katie sighed. "We have to come back home sometime."

He nodded and started across the street.

She followed him, feeling a well of tension grow within her as she opened the door to Drew's house and went in.

The house was empty.

She made dinner for the two of them, not surprised when Drew didn't come home.

Since school was in session, she made Jordan go to bed at nine o'clock. A little bit after, she went herself.

She lay awake. Very late, Drew came home. He didn't come near her door. She made no move toward his.

She woke early the next morning—very early.

She woke Jordan and went downstairs, but Drew was already gone.

Jordan was amazed that he could have come home so late and gone back to work so early.

Katie wasn't. He didn't want to be around her, and he was determined not to make her feel as if she needed to rush to her house.

"He's very busy. I don't think we'll see a lot of him this week," she warned Jordan.

He gave her a baleful look. "I'm not dumb, Mom. You've had a fight with him again."

"Jordan—"

"Don't mess this up, Mom. Please."

"Jordan, you just can't make people into what you want them to be! Come on—you've got to get to school."

He was sulky when she dropped him off. Well, he would have to live with it. She felt her nerves twisting tighter and tighter.

She went back for her cameras and film and started to drive around the city, accustomed to the terrible traffic and driving as if she had eyes all around her head.

She started to take pictures of people rebuilding. They were good pictures. She mentally placed them in the book she would put together.

Everything she had sent off to magazines and papers had been bought. She didn't know whether to be glad that she was doing all right or feel guilty that she was making money that was in any way touched by the dreadful storm.

At eleven, she ran out of film.

She told herself she was only going downtown to buy more film. But she kept driving until she arrived at the main branch of the library.

She went through everything again. She reread the account of Drew's father's death, about his horrible fall and what a shock it had been. He'd been almost like a goat on scaffolding and steel framework. No one had seen quite what had happened. There had been other men in the work area, but no one had been with him.

She flicked through what she had already read; she felt that she should be seeing something, and she didn't know what. At last, she turned off the machine and sat thinking for awhile. It was time to go get Jordan.

Again, Drew Cunningham had managed to stay out of his own house the majority of the night. She had fallen asleep, waiting to hear his door open and close.

In the morning, he was gone again.

But it didn't matter, Katie decided.

Because it was Friday.

She didn't do anything all day except shop for a dress. At three she picked up Jordan from school, and they went to Drew's to prepare for the party. She had chosen a short, midnight-blue velvet dress that seemed to deepen the color of her eyes and went well with her honey blond hair.

She liked the way the dress moved on her. It was sleeveless and nicely molded at the bodice.

She told her reflection that she looked fine, and then she remembered that the exquisite Andrea would be among the guests.

It was all right. Katie decided she could hold her own.

At four-thirty she drove to the Hunnicunn office and parked. She slipped into the downstairs reception area and was relieved to find Reva there, as she had promised. ''Let's get upstairs. Drew is still in his office—he has a shower in there and all—and just in case, you can meet everyone you want to meet before he makes his appearance.''

''Come on, Jordan,'' Katie urged her son.

His powder blue eyes were as hard as Drew's could be.

A little too much bonding had gone on between her son and Drew, she decided. She felt weak and uneasy, worried about what she was doing to Jordan.

But it wasn't time to feel fainthearted. She went with Reva to the elevators and they went to the executive floor, where the party seemed to be in full swing already.

The food had been catered. Delicious-looking finger foods were set out in trays all about them, and attractively dressed servers were moving around, allowing the Hunnicunn employees to sweep up tall, thin glasses of champagne. Katie found herself with a glass, and saw that Jordan—bless him, he would never know how much—was already playing with the twins, stooping down to talk with the pair as they came forward with Drew's secretary.

"Katie, my husband, Cliff Kennedy," Reva said, introducing her to a tall, dark-haired man with a quick smile and handsome face. Katie liked him instantly, noting the way he stood by Reva's side, politely greeted Katie and kept an eye on his offspring at the same time. "Darling, I'm going to introduce Katie around," Reva told him.

"Go right ahead. I'm fine here, you know that."

Katie smiled at him and felt her arm tugged as Reva led her through a group of women to an older man with silvering dark hair. She tried to estimate his age. He wasn't sixty yet, she thought. He was in very good shape.

"Harry!" Reva said. "Just the fellow I'm looking for. Katie is a friend of Drew's. I want her to meet all the people important in our lives, and you're certainly that! Katie, Harry Easton. Harry, Mrs. Katie Wells."

Harry smiled. He looked nice in the tux he was wearing, a well-built man with the weathered features of one who worked outdoors. He took Katie's hand firmly. "How nice to meet you, Mrs. Wells."

"Katie lives—"

"Across the street from Drew. Of course. In the cul-de-sac," Harry said.

Katie gasped. "Yes, of course! I saw you come into my driveway one day."

He nodded. "Came to see Giles. We want to make sure these roofs are right this time!"

"What are we doing?" a masculine voice asked. "Sam! Sam Jaffe, Katie Wells, a friend—and neighbor, as Harry has pointed out—of Drew's."

"Very nice to meet you, Mrs. Wells," the man said. She recognized him from the newspaper pictures. He was older now, of course. And he reminded her very much of a basset hound, with his long features and soulful eyes. He was in his sixties, at least, she thought. "We're sorry about you losing your home."

"Thousands of people lost their homes," Katie assured him. "And actually, mine is close to being repaired. You've all worked very hard."

"We've worked too hard on lots of them!" a husky, feminine voice volunteered.

Andrea. She seemed more stunning than the first time Katie had seen her. She was in a bloodred sequined dress that clung to her like a second skin. The short dress had a deep scooped neckline and no back. She offered a dazzling smile as she moved into their group. "Hello, Katie, the neighbor—right?"

Katie smiled sweetly. Maybe Drew didn't like Andrea, but she was suddenly convinced that Andrea liked Drew. Too much. Despite her half-dozen husbands, she was on her own here, and the taunt seemed a little too tense not to mean something.

"Well," Katie said, "for the moment, I'm the live-in rather than the neighbor. There's been wonderful work done, but my house isn't quite ready yet."

"How convenient for you," Andrea purred.

"Very," Katie agreed.

"Well, Mrs. Wells, since your temporary roommate doesn't seem to be about, perhaps you'd like me to give you a tour of our offices. We're doing some work on them now, of course, but we can skirt the construction area. Let me take you—"

"Excuse me."

Katie felt chills streak up her spine as their group was interrupted once again.

This time by Drew. Katie turned. He was in a tux, tall, dark, his hair damp and sleek, eyes gold and piercing. She'd never seen him quite so attractive—or dangerous.

"I'm afraid Mrs. Wells can't stay this evening," he said, apologizing to Andrea. "She has a heavy work-load tomorrow morning. Katie, come on, and I'll see you out."

He had a firm grip on her wrist and had her moving before she could protest. She tried to smile a goodbye to the men she had just met and signal a frantic call for help to Reva.

"Drew, Jordan—"

"I'm sure Jordan is fine with the boys. And since he's really your guest this evening, Reva, you and Cliff can drop him by on your way home."

"Drew, you can't be leaving!" Andrea protested.

The elevator came. Drew practically dragged Katie onto it, spinning to face the others as the doors closed on them.

"Just for awhile," he said, and his burning gaze fell on Katie. "Just long enough to see to Mrs. Wells."

The doors closed. And for a moment, Katie felt as if she was alone with a furious demon who was ready to strangle her.

But he didn't look at her. He stared straight ahead at the closed elevator doors, his fingers around her wrist, and said, "I told you to stay out of it."

"Your sister needed Jordan—"

"My sister should have her head examined."

"Drew, this doesn't make sense—"

"Katie, get this. I did it, it's my signature on the work orders, and if there's anything else going on, we'll find it from within."

The elevator doors opened to the ground floor. She found herself being dragged into the parking lot.

"Give me your keys," he said.

She gritted her teeth. He wrenched her purse from her hands and dug around until he found them. He opened her car door and forcefully urged her into the driver's seat.

"My son—"

"Will be right along. He's fine. Your questions are going to get you into trouble."

"Drew—"

"Dammit, go home, Katie!"

He slammed the door and stepped back. Exasperated, furious—humiliated!—she twisted her key in the ignition and started the car. She jerked out of the parking lot.

He was keeping Jordan! Of all the nerve. She drove about a block down the highway then pulled off into a side street. She was shaking.

She waited, gathering herself, then pulled out on the highway. She came to a stop at a makeshift sign. While she waited for the opposing traffic to go, she noticed that the headlights of the car behind her were blazing into hers. The driver was close, too close. Right on top of her. She didn't like it.

Katie drove on. She didn't think anything more about the car behind her—she was busy seething over Drew's treatment.

She made a left turn onto the street that would bring her to the cul-de-sac.

The road was dark, nearly pitch black. There wasn't another car in sight.

But there was a car behind her.

Its bumper slammed into hers. She hadn't been expecting the sudden impetus, and her car was easily shoved to the left, almost onto the embankment.

Just beyond the embankment, there was a canal.

Frightened, Katie looked into the rearview mirror. The headlights were streaming so brightly that she couldn't make out the car or driver. She gained control of her vehicle and slammed her foot on the gas.

Not fast enough.

The car slammed into hers again, hard.

And this time her car went careening onto the embankment, pitching downward, straight for the canal. Katie pumped on the brakes, but the wheels refused to catch in the muddy earth. She screamed, bracing herself as she began to hurl wildly toward the water.

Chapter 11

Katie held tightly onto the steering wheel as she careened through mud and foliage. She'd have to get out of the car. She couldn't panic; she just had to get out of the car...

But the car didn't slide into the canal. It hit the jagged stump of a tree and slammed to a halt. Katie was wearing her seat belt, but the crash brought her head slamming against the side of the car.

Blackness exploded before her eyes.

Sometime later, she became aware of a voice coming to her from out of a fog. She was dimly aware of something around her. Something soft. And then there were arms. Lifting her.

"Katie, Katie!"

She heard the sound of sirens and managed to open her eyes.

Drew was there, crouched by her car. The hood was open and steam poured out of the radiator into the darkness. She stared at Drew, still trying to gather her wits. Her head hurt terribly.

"Katie, Katie, I'm sorry. I should have come with you, I wasn't trying to be such a bastard, I simply don't want you involved. I should have never let you drive!"

He thought she had driven into the canal because she had been upset or angry!

"No!" she whispered.

"You're going back to your father's," he continued, his passion bringing his eyes to a golden sizzle against the darkness of the night. "God, I was so wrong to try to bring you back, and now this—"

"I didn't drive off the road!" she managed to get out.

"What?"

"I was slammed off, Drew, someone was behind me."

"Katie, you were knocked out, you don't know what—"

"I know exactly what I'm saying, Drew!" Katie insisted, fingers on his muddied shirt as she struggled against him. "I'm telling you, there was a car behind me that slammed into me and did this!"

He was silent for a minute, but his eyes narrowed and she realized suddenly that he believed her, no matter what he said. "That makes it worse, Katie. You're going to your dad's, and I'll drag you all the way and make sure he keeps you there by force, if that's necessary."

"Drew—"

She broke off because the sounds of the sirens had grown too loud. An ambulance and a police car were coming off the road.

"How did they come so quickly?" Katie whispered.

"Car phone," Drew said. "Over here!" he called out.

Katie found herself suddenly surrounded, stretched out on the ground with brilliant lights flashing into her eyes. She said she was just fine—Drew told the paramedic she had a lump like a tomato on the side of her head.

While one of the paramedics took her pulse, the cop asked her if she could answer questions. Drew said she should get to a hospital.

Katie insisted she could talk.

She described what had happened.

"What kind of car was it?" the cop asked Katie.

"I don't know. I didn't see it all. I saw the lights. There was such a glare out here ..."

The cop wrote down everything she said. The paramedics brought a stretcher.

"I'm all right—"

"You're going to the hospital," Drew insisted.

"But—"

The cop, the paramedics, everyone seemed to think she needed to get to an emergency room. She probably had a concussion—how severe, they didn't know.

"But no one can do anything—"

"They can keep you for observation," Drew said firmly.

"Your husband's right, ma'am," a paramedic told her. "We need to bring you in."

"I'm not his wife," she told the man. "And I don't have to—"

"So you're not my wife. Officer Jenkins can make you go, then," Drew said, his voice cold.

She didn't get a chance to protest. She found herself rolled onto the stretcher and carried to the waiting ambulance.

"Jordan—"

"I'll go to Reva, and she'll bring him home with her," Drew said.

Katie leaned back, frustrated, her head pounding. Drew would come with her to the hospital, surely, and she could talk to him, reason with him...

But though he seemed desperately worried about her, he didn't follow her into the ambulance. She heard him speaking to one of the men, but then the door slammed shut, the siren went on and she felt herself being driven onto the road.

They were extremely kind, efficient and quick at the hospital, despite the fact that the building had endured some damage during the storm and there were boards in many places where windows had once been. Katie was checked, poked, prodded, studied, X-rayed and scanned, then put in a little flowered hospital gown with no back. In her pleasant, private room for the night, she was told that she definitely did have a concussion, not too serious, but that she would be watched anyway.

The room had a bed, a television and a comfortable, big chair—and Drew. He had been home—or somewhere—because he had changed. He was wearing clean jeans and a dark knit shirt. His hair was slicked back, leaving the lines of his face striking, sharp—and more haggard than she had ever seen him.

"Hi," he told her.

"Hi," she said warily.

"How are you feeling?"

"I have a headache," she admitted. "What about Jordan?"

"He's with Reva. She's staying at our house tonight with the kids. Tomorrow, when you're released, I'll pick you up, and then swing by Reva's for Jordan and take you both to the airport."

"Drew, I don't want to go back to Orlando—"

"Katie," he interrupted, leaning forward, "you're going back."

She couldn't argue anymore, not that night. They had given her something that was easing the pain in her head, but stealing away her strength to protest.

"This is ridiculous. Some drunk hits me—"

"Katie, it was no drunk."

"Who could know that I'm interested in whatever is going on at Hunnicunn?"

"I know, my mother knows, my sister knows. Lots of people know about your house, and the entire world knows about construction codes and shoddy materials down here now. You showed up at that party—"

"If everyone knows so much, it must be common knowledge that I'm sleeping with you, as well!" she said. "It was natural for me to be at that party."

He was silent. "*Were* sleeping with me, Katie. I want you out of here, out of my house, out of my life. Do you understand?"

"I want you out of my hospital room!" she told him, very close to tears.

"I'll be in this chair through the night," he said.

"I can have you thrown out," she whispered.

"You can try."

She turned her back on him. The violent action hurt her head all over again.

Knowing Drew, he probably did have some kind of sway with the hospital. She closed her eyes. They had warned she might feel sick. She didn't feel sick. Just empty. She'd lost her home, and that had been okay. Now she had lost her car. And, hey, that was okay, too.

But suddenly, though he remained near her, she felt the cold distance that seemed to separate her from Drew. She had lost him, as well.

"You keep telling me that you're the responsible person!" she whispered. "And if you are, then I haven't anything to fear. It's foolish for you to assume—"

"Maybe I am responsible," he said. "I was there awfully quickly, Katie. Maybe I'm guilty of more than you imagine. Maybe you should be just as far away from me as possible. Has that occurred to you?" he asked.

Her back remained to him. His words seemed to scratch down her spine.

He had arrived at the accident scene first. How, why? She had assumed he had been going back to his party.

She turned to stare at him, heedless of the pain in her head. "It's no good," she told him huskily. "You left the party to come after me. You were afraid of what I might do, or else you were worried about me. That's why you came upon me so quickly."

"You haven't the sense to see danger, Katie! Even when your car has been totaled and you're in a hospital bed!"

"You can't just assume my accident had anything to do with you!"

"Rest, Katie," he said firmly.

"Drew—"

He stood up and walked out of the room. She closed her eyes, then realized that she couldn't fight the medication.

She must have dozed. She awakened when a doctor flicked light in her eyes, telling her that he was sorry, but she was—excuse the term—a head case, and he had to make sure she was doing all right.

Drew was in his chair, a coffee cup in his hand.

She wanted to talk to him, reason with him. But she was too weary and too drugged.

When she opened her eyes again, it was morning. Drew was gone. Breakfast was being set on her table and a cheerful nurse was telling her good morning.

Her head didn't seem to hurt at all anymore.

"Tell, me, please," Katie asked the nurse, "do you know what happened to Mr. Cunningham?"

"Yes, indeed. He had a few errands to run. The doctor will release you around eleven, and he'll be back for you then," the nurse assured her. "How're you feeling?" she asked Katie.

"Good," Katie told her, taking a sip of coffee.

"Honestly," the nurse said, making a ticking sound, "the accidents since Andrew are just awful! It's such a strange thing, that storm. So many terrible things happening! But then again . . ."

"What?" Katie said.

The nurse shrugged and smiled. "We've all been trying to put in a few hours in the tent hospitals south of here, looking after all the displaced people. Andrew brought about so many broken bones and gashes and all, some serious, some not so serious. But we've managed to see all kinds of children down there who have never been to a doctor, who have never had even the minimal shots. So, in a way, some good things have happened. And, it's interesting to see how the community has bonded."

"The rainbow after the storm?" Katie asked.

"Something like that. Well, if you need anything, just hit your call button. The doctor should be in soon, and then, hopefully, you'll be on your way."

Drew pressed his fingers against his temple and closed his eyes at his desk.

It had happened. He didn't know why he had been so worried, what had given him a premonition that he had to get Katie out of town. Maybe there hadn't been a reason for him to be worried about her looking into things, but somehow, he had just been afraid, and now...

It was common knowledge that Katie owned the house across from his. One of the three that had gone down. But Ted Barlow might have wanted to rip the company apart, just as Seth and Susan might have.

What would have been found? His signature on the work orders...

Except that his signature had been forged, he was certain of it. Half the records had mysteriously disappeared, and Jeannie had been at a loss. But he had found a copy of one of the work orders, misfiled, and he had stared at it for hours. The signature was his— but it wasn't his. He was certain of it.

Who, who, who?

He had to think. Last night...

Katie had come here, Katie had seen all the major players. Andrea, Drew, Reva. Harry Easton and Sam Jaffe. Then, of course, there was Giles...

But Giles hadn't been here last night. Did that make him guilty, or innocent?

Katie had gone. And he had come back to the party, thinking he would stay. But he had known he couldn't stay—not with the way he had sent her from the office. He'd been worried sick even before he'd nearly driven by her smashed car.

He thought she'd driven off the road herself. Until she told him she'd been hit.

Then...

He had wanted to go to the hospital with her. He hadn't, because he wanted to see her car before the police towed it. He stood with the officer, waiting for the tow truck, trying to inspect it in the darkness with his car lights and the cop's powerful flashlight.

She'd been bumped, and hard. Bits of black rubber were stuck to the smashed chrome on her car.

And maybe...

Just a tiny line of yellow paint that didn't belong.

He tried to remember what he had done after he had sent Katie away. He'd come upstairs. He'd talked to his sister, to his secretary. Sean Carson, Giles's assistant, had come in. Giles was still at one of the work sites, Sean had said.

Giles?

That didn't seem possible...

All right, so Giles hadn't been there.

Andrea had. He had heard her voice loud and clear when he had decided he was getting a headache and had to go after Katie, just to make sure she got home all right.

Which she hadn't.

He tapped a pen on his desk. He had seen Andrea. Giles might have been anywhere, and when he'd come back, neither Sam Jaffe nor Harry Easton had been in the area, either.

"Sam? Harry? Impossible!" he said softly.

But it wasn't impossible. That Andrea might be guilty seemed impossible—she had been at the office. He wasn't guilty—he knew that. Nor Reva, nor his mother.

That narrowed down the field. When the truly impossible was eliminated, then the improbable had to be possible.

But...

He suddenly found herself thinking back. Far back. He closed his eyes again, leaning back in his chair. It was amazing how some memories could stay with you, seeming so small yet so clear years and years later.

He could remember that night, crawling out of bed, hearing his father. Stepping into the hallway and seeing his dad and the others. He remembered exactly how they had been seated around the table, so much younger then, of course. Almost thirty years younger...

His dad, at the head of the table. Sam Jaffe sorrowfully at his side, Harry Easton there, as well, and tall, skinny Trent Waite.

Poor Trent. He'd died of cancer within five years.

He'd been so appalled at the building practices he'd seen.

And Sam...

The first big wind, Sam had said. Shaking his head. He had known.

They couldn't keep building that way, but they had families, they had to keep working...

But A. J. Cunningham had been a fighter. He had made a lot of waves. No one had ever fired him. He'd kept working until the day he died. Why, Harry Easton had told Drew that A.J. had been upset that day, telling Harry that if they weren't given more say, he'd go to the newspapers.

Drew suddenly felt a faint prickling at the back of his neck.

He wondered if...

He stood up and hurried out to Jeannie. "Is everyone in today?"

"Well, one of the secretaries on two is out with the flu—" Jeannie began.

"No, up here. On the executive floors."

"Your sister hasn't come in. Andrea called to say that she wouldn't be coming in at all. Sam and Harry are both here—I believe they went over to see what was going on with some of the repairs at the end of the hall."

"Fine," Drew said. "I'll—I'll be out there myself if anyone needs me."

He hurried past her.

He was suddenly certain that he knew who had forged his name.

And tried to kill Katie. Kill her . . .

Oh, God, and if he was given another chance, he did have more to cover up. More than he had imagined . . .

Ten o'clock, and she was free.

She wasn't waiting for Drew, and she wasn't going to get shipped out of town! Not when she felt as if the truth was just barely eluding her . . .

She called Drew's house and assured Reva that she was all right, then she talked to Jordan—and worked even harder to assure him that she was truly fine.

Then she asked Reva if she and her family would mind staying just a bit longer to watch Jordan.

Reva hesitated. "Katie, isn't Drew coming for you? He made reservations for you on a flight to Orlando for this afternoon."

"He shouldn't have," Katie said. "Listen, Reva, I just want to check one more thing. I'll see you this evening, I promise."

She hung up before Reva could protest. Then she hurried to the elevators, determined to escape before Reva could call her back—or get Drew.

Katie couldn't imagine running around the city in her cocktail dress. Luckily, the hospital gift shop sold some knit tank tops and shorts with flamingos on them, and rubber sandals. Not an outfit she was crazy about, but for the time being, it was just fine.

Once she had changed, she hurried outside and caught a cab. "Downtown," she told the driver. "The main library."

"All right, lady!" It was a good fare from the hospital. He was naturally pleased.

She knew what she wanted. She went to the microfilm machine and drew up the pictures and stories from the day A. J. Cunningham had died. She read through the articles again, and the interviews with both Harry Easton and Sam Jaffe.

She stared at the pictures, touching a face. Yes, the man had been the one who'd come to her house that day. That didn't make him guilty of anything, of course...

But some of the things he said in the article made her suspicious. *"A.J. was such a good man, such a fighter. He didn't worry about keeping his job, like some of us did. He just went right after the big boys."*

Didn't worry about keeping his job...

And some people did. That wasn't a crime, either.

But then again...

"I can't believe it. I was so close to him when it happened. I knew A.J. so well…"

She didn't turn off the machine. She jumped up and ran out of the library, hurrying for the first public phone she could find. She swore when she dropped her quarter.

She dialed Hunnicunn and got Drew's secretary, Jeannie. "Jeannie, I need Drew, quickly, please!"

"Katie, I'm sorry, I can't reach him. He's gone out to the construction area."

"He's out on a job?"

"No—the construction area in this building. Darn, Katie, he just left to walk out there, he was here just a second ago. Can I give him a message?"

"I—no, yes—just tell him that I'm not at the hospital, I'm on my way over. I'll meet him in his office." She hung up, ran out to the street and hailed a cab.

Sixty very anxious minutes later, she reached the Hunnicunn offices. She hurried in and took the elevator directly to the executive floor. The receptionist was not at her desk. Nor was Jeannie at hers.

It was lunchtime, Katie realized sickly. She wondered if Drew had gotten her message.

She hurried into his office, but he wasn't there. Frustrated, worried, ready to burst, she sank down on his sofa to wait.

A second later, she bolted up. There was a man in the doorway, watching her.

It wasn't Drew.

"Katie!" he said softly. "How nice to see you again!"

She forced a smile to her lips. She tried desperately to hide what she knew.

"Hi, to you, too."

"We were so sorry to hear about your accident last night!"

"Yes, well, I'm really fine, thanks."

"Looking for Drew?"

"Yes."

She needed to reach the phone. Or the door. Maybe she just needed to scream.

"He's in the construction area. Want me to take you to him?"

"Ah, no, I—I'll just wait. No, you know what? I think I'll just go get some lunch." She smiled cheerfully and started out of the office.

He stood in her way.

"I don't think so, Katie. I'm so sorry. Really, I am."

"You wouldn't dare hurt me here!" she said. She tried to make the words forceful.

He smiled. "I don't want to hurt you, Katie. I want to kill you. It's got to be an accident, of course."

"Sorry, I just won't oblige you," she began, but then again...

Maybe she would. He had a two-by-four in his hands, a simple construction board. And even as she started to scream, the board came crashing down on her.

He bent quickly, throwing her over his shoulder even as the blackness burst upon her vision once again...

* * *

When she came to, it was still dark, and her head was reeling. She struggled and felt rock-hard hands press her down on strong shoulders.

"Almost there!" he grunted.

She ducked as they went through plastic screening hung from the wall separating two areas.

"You don't need to do this!" Katie said. "Roof staples were legal. Drew would never prosecute you."

She was lifted and set down. She started to twist around, then realized that there was nothing beneath her.

He had carried her out to where the flooring had been ripped away. She was balanced on a steel girder.

And beneath her was darkness, a void, empty...

"This is exactly what you did to A. J. Cunningham!" she whispered.

"So you knew," Harry Easton said with a sigh, shoving on her shoulders. Katie gritted her teeth, fighting his push at first, then crawling swiftly and for all she was worth along the steel framework. One of her rubber sandals fell off.

She didn't hear it hit the floor below for a long, long time...

"Katie!"

She had moved far ahead. He couldn't see her, she thought. She went still, hoping he might not hear her, either.

"There's no way back in, Katie, except by me. You can't just hold on there forever."

Yes, she could, she thought, arms and legs wrapped around the girder.

"Katie, I've got a gun. It isn't a magnum or anything. I bought it just because I'm an older man, you know. Failing just a little bit. Out at lonely work sites upon occasion."

She held her breath and prayed. She wanted to tell him that he'd surely be arrested if he *shot* her, and she wanted to ask him why he had done any of this, but she didn't dare speak and give away her position.

"I'm coming, Katie," he told her. "I'm out on the girder now myself, and I've been doing this for many years. I've been making a living at it, you know. You just give absolute quality all the time, Katie. You can't make money that way. Drew will never see it, but you're right, he won't prosecute me—" He broke off and started to laugh. "I can see you, Katie. And I'm coming for you. Make it easy for both of us. Isn't the fear terrible? Wouldn't you rather end it without the suffering?"

Yes, it was terrible. It hurt to breathe! She was trembling, sweating. Sweating terribly. She was afraid she'd lose her grip...

But no matter how terrible, life was worth any price. He didn't seem to realize that. Maybe he'd never had a son like Jordan to live for...

Or someone to love, like Drew.

Drew. Who had been so angry with her. Who had wanted so badly to get her away. Who had been so afraid because...

He loved her, as well.

"Drew will know!" she cried out. "He knows last night was no accident, he knows, he'll hunt you down—"

"He doesn't know about his father," Harry said. "And he'll never be certain that I was anywhere near you—"

Harry broke off suddenly. Katie wondered why, then she heard shuffling. A definite footstep in the darkness. They weren't alone anymore. Someone was with him.

"He knows about his father!" came a deep, husky, masculine voice.

Her heart stopped beating, then began anew in a wild, frantic rhythm.

Drew had come. He had found her. Somehow he had found her out here with this murderer.

"Drew, be careful!" Katie warned. "There's no flooring here."

"I know, Katie."

Then she saw him, a swift, supple shadow, bearing down on Harry Easton.

And Harry Easton started backing away from him.

"I can reach her before you can, Drew. I'll kill her, I swear I will."

"Don't be an idiot. I want to strangle you, but I won't. When you killed my father, it was first-degree, premeditated murder. But you can get a good lawyer, Harry. Maybe you'll get life. But life in prison would be better than dying my father's death, Harry. Falling, breaking, taking your last breath in agony!"

Katie, terrified, winced, feeling the pain of Drew's words seep into her.

"I'm telling you, get away! I'm a damned strong man, Drew, I'll take the girl down—"

Harry broke off again, this time with a scream. He fell toward Katie, reaching out for her. She saw his eyes, saw his fingers stretching and stretching...

She screamed, backing away on the girder with all the courage she could muster. "Drew!" she heard herself crying in terror, for Drew was fighting with the man. The two of them were rolling on the girder.

"No!" she shrieked, covering her ears against the terrible scream that suddenly pierced the air. She couldn't see, it was still so shadowy, but one of the men had fallen over the edge.

The scream abruptly ended with a terrible crash.

One man remained, breathing heavily, gasping, just feet away from Katie...

"Oh, God!" she screamed.

But then she heard his voice. Drew's voice. "Katie?"

"Drew, oh, thank God, Drew..."

"Katie, stay still."

He was carefully moving toward her. She was still frightened. Shaking. She'd never make it back.

She had to make it back.

The only other way was...

Harry's way.

She felt his hands around her shoulders. "Katie, hold tight to my belt. It's not so hard to walk these things if you're used to them, but they can be treacherous. We'll stay down and take it on our knees. All right?"

She couldn't let him know how terrified she was.

"Yes!"

She inched behind him, holding carefully to him. Once she started to lose her balance and shift to the side.

"Hold, Katie!"

She did. He stayed still until she adjusted her balance. They started moving again. "No one was supposed to be out here. This area was boarded off," Drew said.

"He must have ripped down the board when I was out," Katie said.

"You fainted?"

"He—he knocked me out with a two-by-four."

Drew paused. She felt his tension. "Oh, Drew! I'm so sorry. I didn't really know for sure that he had killed your father, but he had disagreed with him, and he was afraid that A.J. might cost him his job!"

"And he worked with me. For years," Drew said bitterly. "I loved him like an uncle."

"Drew . . ."

"We're here, Katie. Let go for a second." She did, trusting him. For a moment, it seemed that she was alone, floating in darkness.

Then she was lifted up, into his arms. He walked through the darkness until they returned to the plastic sheeting, then over the board Harry had broken down.

Into a carpeted hallway.

Drew was covered with plaster. She was certain that she must be well powdered with it herself.

Suddenly she felt his arms shaking, even as he held her. He cupped her cheek and kissed her lips very tenderly.

"Dear God, Katie, if he'd managed to hurt you..."

"I'm fine, Drew." But she wasn't fine. She was shaking. "I love you," she told him. "I—I love you."

He smiled, holding her against him as he started down the hallway toward the sound section of the building.

"We've got to call the police. And I'll have to change your flight reservations."

"Change them?" Katie whispered. "But, Drew—"

"You've got to go to Orlando."

"But—"

"I know, I'm not your husband, and you're not my wife, and you don't have to do anything that I tell you. That's why I want to change all that. Quickly."

"What?"

"Well, I really like your dad, even if he is fooling around with my mother. So I think that even if it's small—if that's all right, I just don't want to wait on this—your father and Jordan should be there for our wedding. Not that I think you're ever going to listen to anything I tell you to do after we're married, but then . . . it's worth a try."

She stared at him, then smiled very slowly.

"Is that—a proposal?" she asked him.

"It is. Will you marry me, Katie?"

"What a way to get out of replacing my house!" she said.

He shook his head.

"Then . . . ?" Katie said.

He paused and kissed her again.

"Because I love you, Katie. Because I just wasn't whole until after that storm. Until I went out into the wind and rain and found you."

"Oh, Drew!" she said, and caught his nape, and kissed him hard.

"Say yes, Katie," he urged her.

"Yes," she whispered.

He laughed softly, exultantly, and started down the hallway. "This marriage thing might work after all!" he told her.

And for the moment, she didn't protest, she just clung to him and thought about how very much she loved him.

* * * * *

Author's Note

Andrew and its aftermath brought out some of the best human qualities—courage, kindness, and in many instances, valiant sacrifices to the needs of others. Friendships were formed, bonds were made that will never be broken. The face of South Florida will never be the same.

I managed not to be home for Andrew—the storm struck in late August and my family and I were on our way home after the summer vacation. Early Saturday morning, I had spoken with my mother and we knew there was a storm out there, a small one at that time, and perhaps heading anywhere from the Keys to the Carolinas. Andrew grew to intensity with amazing swiftness—and aimed directly at Dade County. We came into our Virginia hotel room that night just in time to learn that our home might well be demol-

ished. From our distance, we had electricity and television, and painful, terrible glimpses of what was
going on. The morning was a horror as we tried to get
through on the phone to family and friends; we were
frantic just to see if they had all made it okay. We were
lucky; we were able to get through and find out that
our family and close friends were all right, just dazed
and stunned, and trying to pick up some of the pieces.
Despite everything that we had seen and heard, coming home was still a shock. Andrew's power was simply extraordinary. It truly looked as if bombs had gone
off in many areas of Dade County.

A newspaper reported that thirty-five lives were
lost directly to the storm—people struck by debris,
crushed, drowned—and another eighty-five lives lost
to the terrible circumstances surrounding it, including a large number of tragic auto accidents. Over
eighty thousand homes were lost. And there are still
countless miles of destruction to be seen. It will take
years to rebuild. Some people have moved out, and
some will stay.

We have learned some lessons from this storm, lessons that some people have known for years, and
others just learned in a most painful fashion. Nothing could have changed the force of such a storm, but
it is equally true that some of the terrible devastation
could have been eased if building codes had been more
vigorously acknowledged, and if many builders had
not only tried to adhere to the codes, but remembered
that our houses are our homes and our *shelters*. My
father-in-law is a retired electrician. Years ago I can
remember when some of his co-workers were speak-

ing together at a picnic. "One big wind," they had said. Andrew was all of that and more, an incredible force, and yet we can only hope that in the future, we will do all that we can to minimize the losses, human and material, of such a force.

SILHOUETTE
Sensation

COMING NEXT MONTH

TO HOLD AN EAGLE Justine Davis

Bitter experience had proved to Chandra Lansing that every man had his price. Yet here was Linc Reese (brother to Shiloh from *Cool Under Fire*) ready to track down her would-be murderer, demanding nothing in return. But how could she let him risk his life for her?

BLACK TREE MOON Kathleen Eagle

He Who Dares

Race Latimer, who appeared briefly in *Bad Moon Rising*, had always drifted from town to town, fire to fire and woman to woman. But suddenly preacher's daughter Hannah Quinn had him hotter than he'd ever been. Was he going to get burned *off* duty?

SWEET ANNIE'S PASS Marilyn Pappano

Josiah Miller had once found happiness farming his land and raising a family. But now, until the arrival of Annabeth Gibbs, he spent his days pining for the child he'd lost and the love he'd never really had. Annabeth had come to uncover her past and nobody was going to drive her away—not even stubborn Josiah Miller! It was a war of wills.

FROM A DISTANCE Emilie Richards

They were fire and ice—mated in wedded bliss. But their happily-ever-after turned into estrangement and, finally, divorce. Yet when Lindsey was rushed to hospital, Stefan couldn't get to her bedside fast enough. She was clearly physically ill, but nothing he knew seemed to help. Just when they'd both acknowledged their feelings were they going to run out of time together? Was it something to do with her UFO sighting?

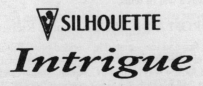

COMING NEXT MONTH FROM

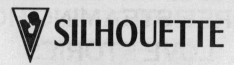 **SILHOUETTE**

Intrigue

*Danger, deception and desire—
from Silhouette...*

LIFE LINE Rebecca York
DEADLY SECRETS Lynn Turner
CRY OF THE WILD Catherine Anderson
BITTERSWEET LEGACY Jenna Ryan

Special Edition

Satisfying romances packed with emotion

MYSTERY WIFE Annette Broadrick
SHADOWS AND LIGHT Lindsay McKenna
LOVING AND GIVING Gina Ferris
MY BABY, YOUR CHILD Nikki Benjamin
WALK IN BEAUTY Ruth Wind
THE PRINCESS OF COLDWATER FLATS
Natalie Bishop

Desire

*Provocative, sensual love stories for the
woman of today*

BEWITCHED Jennifer Greene
I'M GONNA GET YOU Lass Small
MYSTERY LADY Jackie Merritt
THE BRAINY BEAUTY Suzanne Simms
RAFFERTY'S ANGEL Caroline Cross
STEALING SAVANNAH Donna Carlisle

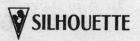

HE WHO DARES

Starting in July, every month in **Silhouette Sensation**, one fabulous, irresistible man will be featured as *He Who Dares*. When Silhouette Sensation's best writers go all-out to create exciting, extraordinary men, it's no wonder if women everywhere start falling in love. Just take a look at what—and who!—we have in store during the next few months.

In July:
MACKENZIE'S MISSION by Linda Howard

In August:
QUINN EISLEY'S WAR by Patricia Gardner Evans

In September:
BLACK TREE MOON by Kathleen Eagle

In October:
CHEROKEE THUNDER by Rachel Lee

He Who Dares. You won't want to miss a single one, but watch out—these men are dangerous!